THE GOLDEN ATLAS FOR CHILDREN

Text by Neil Morris
Illustrated by Illustratori Associati Boni-Galante

A GOLDEN BOOK
Western Publishing Company, Inc.

 Library of Congress Catalog Card Number: 92-72133 ISBN: 0-307-17876-5/ISBN: 0-307-67876-8 (lib. bdg.) A MCMXCV

How to use this atlas

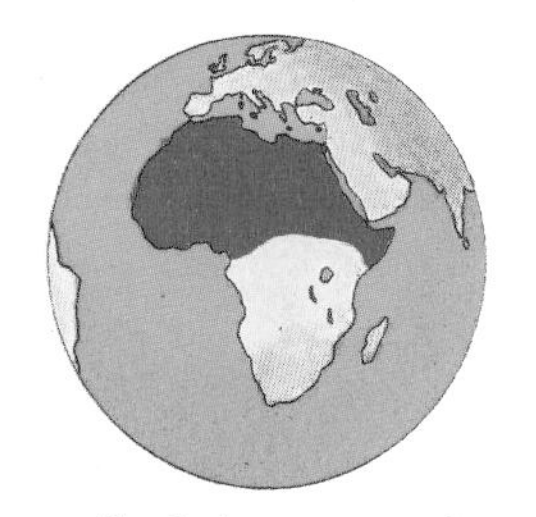

The small globe in each section shows in red where the countries are located.

High areas of ground are shown in two ways: The highest mountains appear to be more pointed and are colored white.

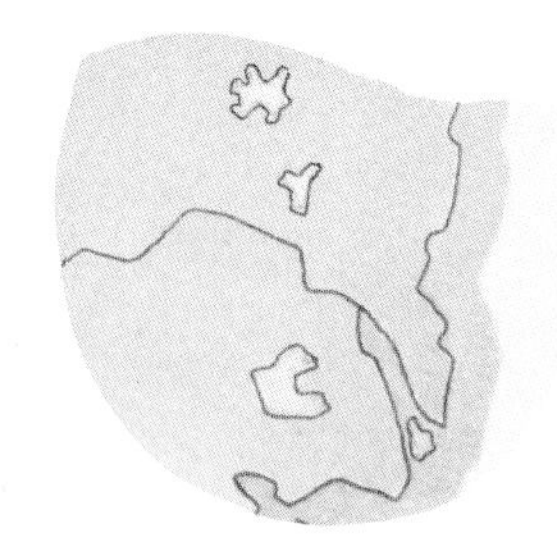

Seas and oceans are colored blue. Small areas of blue on the land are lakes. Rivers are shown as blue lines.

Some lakes shown do not appear all year round but dry up during certain times of the year. These are indicated by broken lines.

Geographical features of special interest are sometimes pinpointed by symbols.

This atlas is a book of maps and information about the countries of the world. Each section has a map of an area of the world, accompanied by an introductory text and information about points of interest.

The maps show geographical features, such as mountains, rivers, and lakes, that are important to a particular area of the world. Capitals are shown for most countries, as well as other noteworthy cities.

Symbols represent areas where, for example, fruits and vegetables might grow or where industries, such as mining or fishing, are located. The symbols also show where plants and animals live. Some symbols locate famous buildings, and others picture people who live in a region.

Red lines mark each country's borders. State borders are shown in green.

Other symbols on the maps may show produce, industry, natural resources, animals, people, vegetation, or mountains.

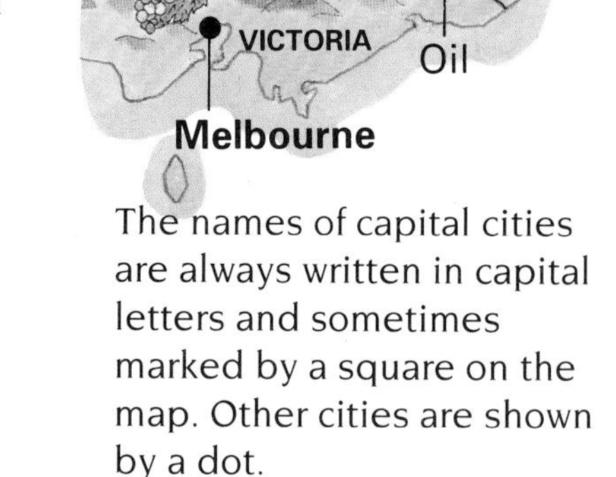

The names of capital cities are always written in capital letters and sometimes marked by a square on the map. Other cities are shown by a dot.

Certain cities have interesting buildings, and in some cases pictures of these buildings mark the city, as well as a square or a dot.

Trees of different types show the various types of vegetation around the world.

Broad-leaved trees grow where the weather is warmer.

Spruce and fir trees grow in cold areas.

Rainforest trees show hot, wet, tropical areas.

The scale lets you estimate the size of each country and how far one place is from another. Each map is drawn to a different scale.

0 400 800 miles

0 600 1200 km

Contents

The World

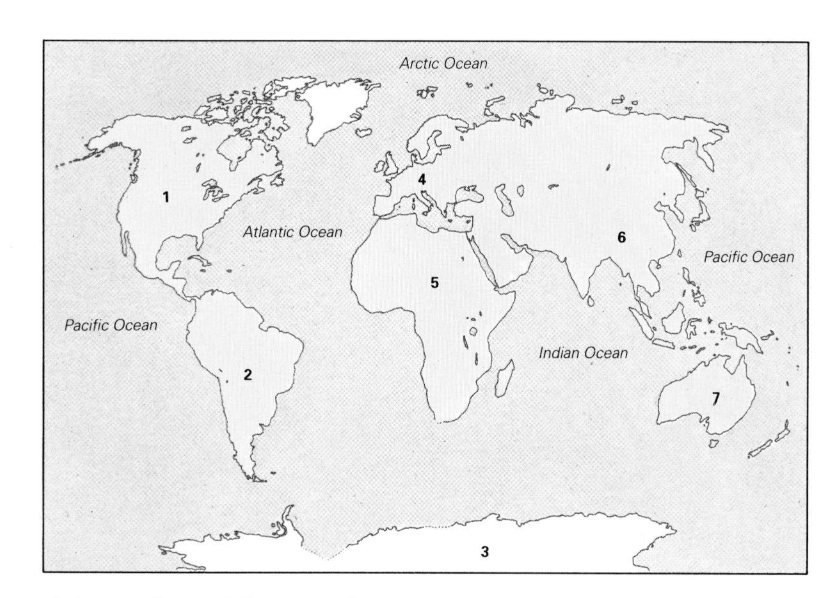

If the surface of the round Earth were stretched out, it would make a flat map of the world, with the Pacific Ocean split in two.

From outer space, the Earth looks blue, since so much of its surface is covered by water. There are 4 major bodies of water—the Pacific, Atlantic, Indian, and Arctic oceans.

The oceans are separated by large areas of land. These are the Earth's 7 continents. The continents of Asia, Africa, and Europe form more than half the Earth's total landmass. North and South America make up a long stretch of land between the Pacific and Atlantic oceans. Antarctica lies around the South Pole. Australia is the smallest continent.

Throughout the world, weather conditions—or climate—are very different. A region's climate is affected by its location, by how high it is above sea level, by how close it is to mountains or oceans, and by local winds.

The Arctic (North Pole) and Antarctic regions are freezing cold. Below the Arctic are frozen

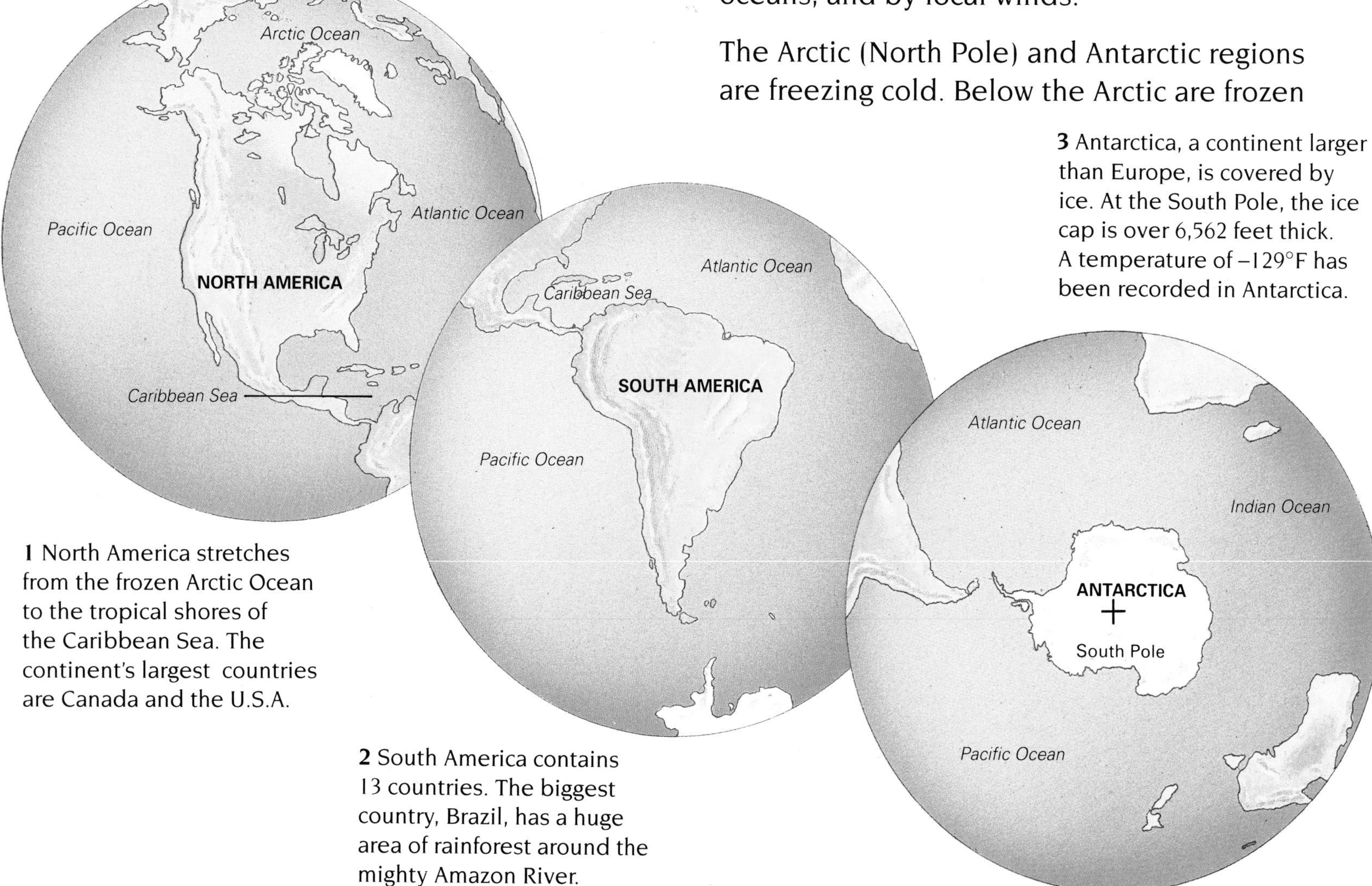

3 Antarctica, a continent larger than Europe, is covered by ice. At the South Pole, the ice cap is over 6,562 feet thick. A temperature of −129°F has been recorded in Antarctica.

1 North America stretches from the frozen Arctic Ocean to the tropical shores of the Caribbean Sea. The continent's largest countries are Canada and the U.S.A.

2 South America contains 13 countries. The biggest country, Brazil, has a huge area of rainforest around the mighty Amazon River.

treeless plains. Farther south are forest regions of spruce and fir trees. In areas of mild climate, there are forests of broad-leaved trees, and nearer the equator are the hot tropical rainforests.

Mild and warm climates produce grasslands, such as the Great Plains of North America. A third of the Earth's land area is desert.

All the continents, except Antarctica and Australia, are divided into countries. The world's nations are not scattered evenly across the planet. More than half of the world's population lives in Asia, while no one lives permanently in Antarctica.

Many of the world's settlements grew up where there were rivers, good soil, natural resources, and minerals. Today, as the world's population continues to grow, more people are moving from rural areas to big cities.

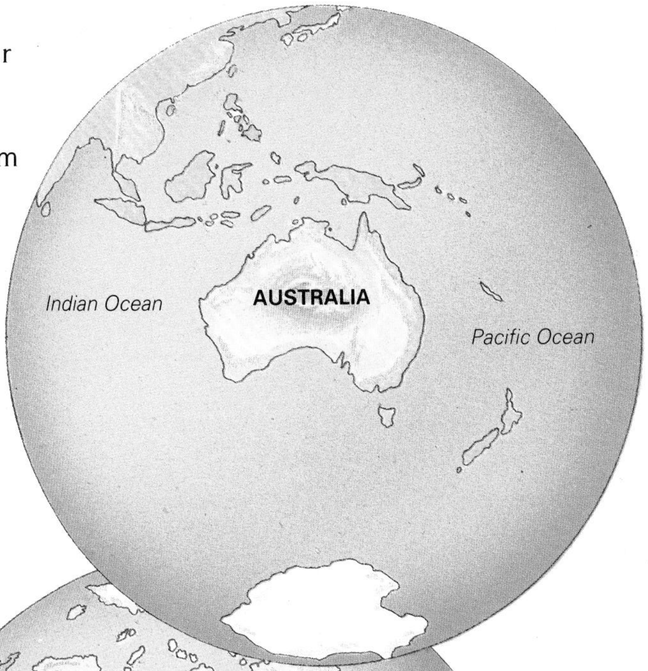

7 Australasia is made up of Australia, New Zealand, Papua New Guinea, and over 20,000 small islands in the Pacific Ocean. Australia has the fewest people, apart from Antarctica.

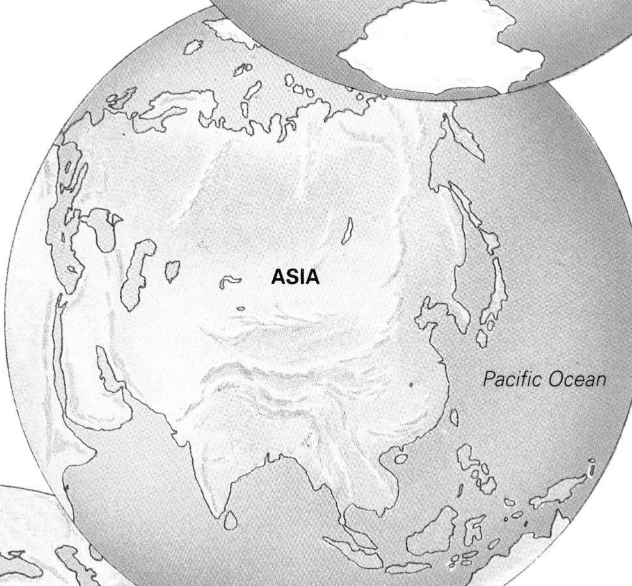

6 Asia is the largest continent and has the most people. Russia is the largest country in the world, and China has more people than any other country. In central Asia, the Himalayas form the highest range of mountains on Earth. This is sometimes called the "rooftop of the world."

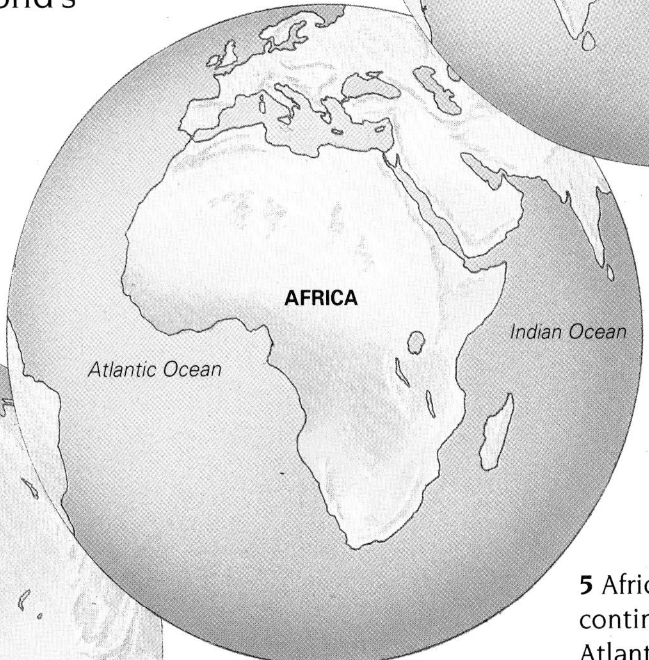

5 Africa, the second-largest continent, lies between the Atlantic and Indian oceans. Much of northern Africa is covered by the Sahara, the world's biggest desert.

4 Europe is made up of many small countries and the western part of Russia. This continent stretches from the cold north of Scandinavia to the warm Mediterranean Sea in the south.

More About . . .

The **Inuit** people live in the Arctic. Some still hunt, but many work as fishermen or miners.

The **CN Tower** in Toronto is 1,185 feet high. It is made of steel and concrete and is the world's highest freestanding structure.

Lumberjacks cut down trees with power saws in Canada's forests. They can make the trees fall just where they want.

The **Royal Canadian Mounted Police** force rode on horseback until 1929. Today aircraft and snowmobiles are often used.

Did You Know?

Canada has two official languages: English and French. One quarter of the people speak French as their first language.

Fantastic shimmering flashes of light often brighten the arctic skies in the north of Canada. They are known as the aurora borealis, or the northern lights.

The world's largest exhibit of complete dinosaur skeletons can be found in a museum near the city of Calgary.

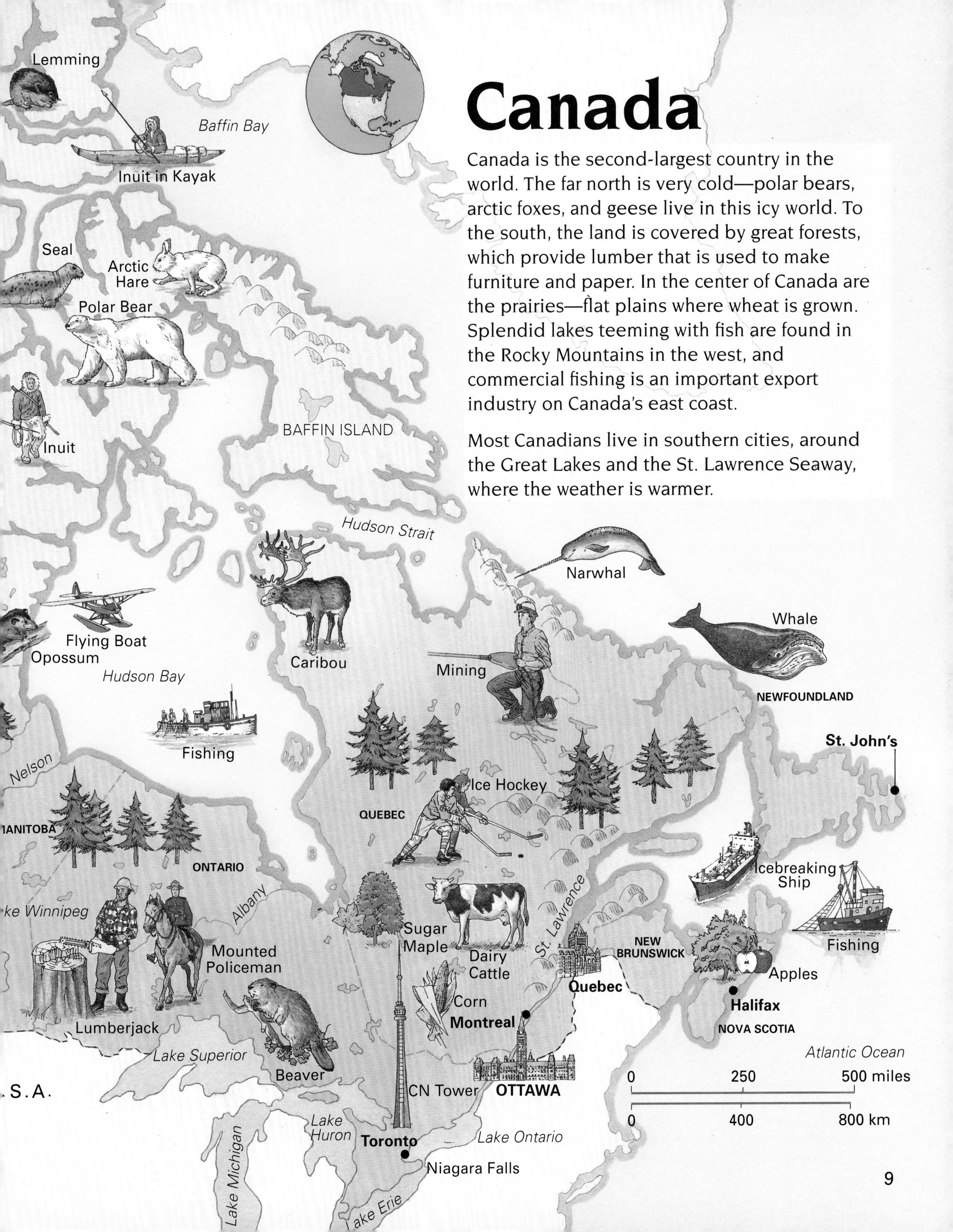

Canada

Canada is the second-largest country in the world. The far north is very cold—polar bears, arctic foxes, and geese live in this icy world. To the south, the land is covered by great forests, which provide lumber that is used to make furniture and paper. In the center of Canada are the prairies—flat plains where wheat is grown. Splendid lakes teeming with fish are found in the Rocky Mountains in the west, and commercial fishing is an important export industry on Canada's east coast.

Most Canadians live in southern cities, around the Great Lakes and the St. Lawrence Seaway, where the weather is warmer.

United States of America

The United States of America is made up of 50 states. Forty-eight lie between Canada to the north and Mexico to the south. The 49th and 50th states are separated from the others: Alaska is west of Canada, while Hawaii is southwest of the mainland in the Pacific Ocean.

The first Americans were Indians, who traveled from Asia in prehistoric times. Europeans began to arrive more than 400 years ago. Later, black Africans were brought to work as slaves—until slavery was ended in 1865. More recently, people from Asia and from Central and South America have moved to the U.S.

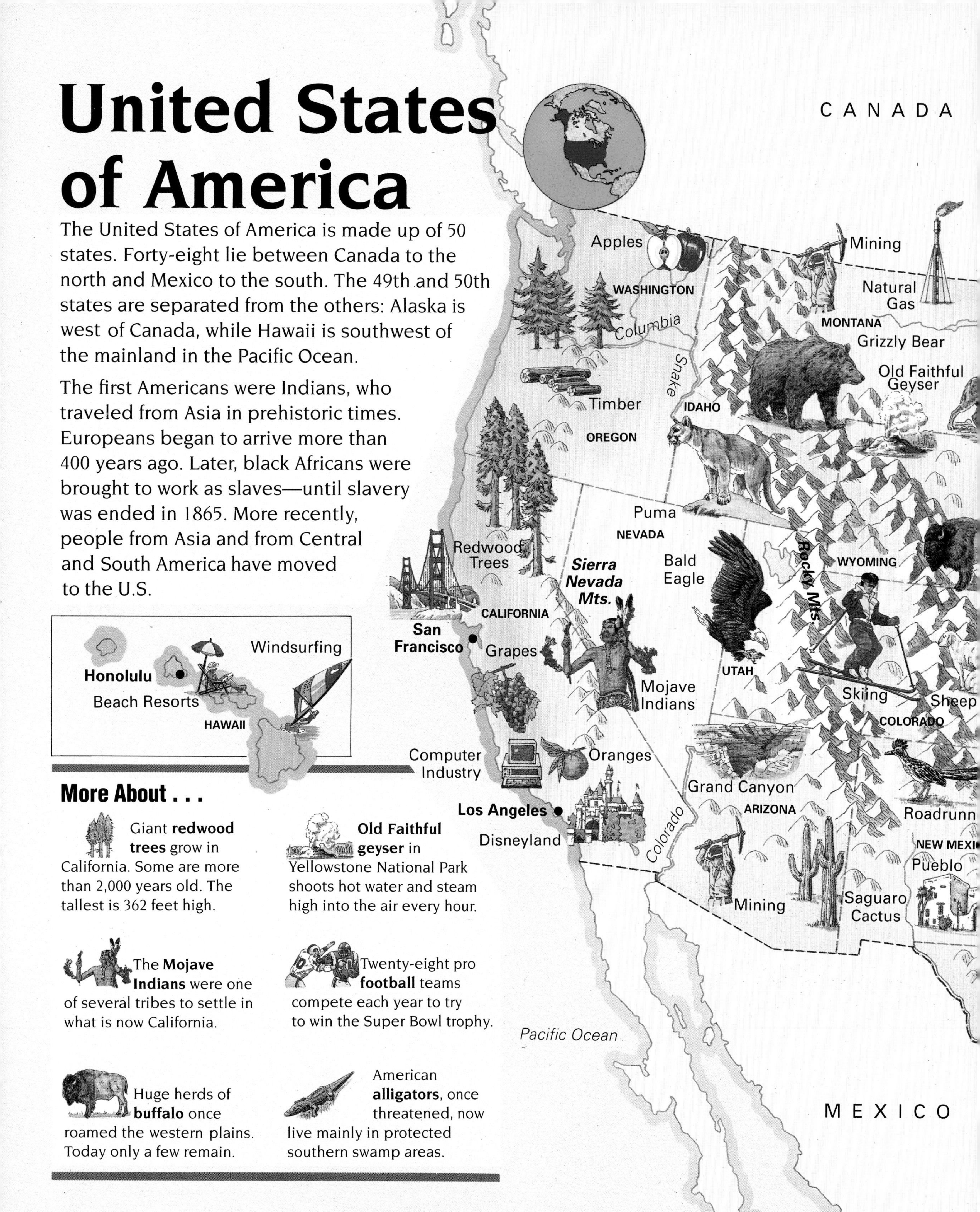

More About . . .

Giant **redwood trees** grow in California. Some are more than 2,000 years old. The tallest is 362 feet high.

Old Faithful geyser in Yellowstone National Park shoots hot water and steam high into the air every hour.

The **Mojave Indians** were one of several tribes to settle in what is now California.

Twenty-eight pro **football** teams compete each year to try to win the Super Bowl trophy.

Huge herds of **buffalo** once roamed the western plains. Today only a few remain.

American **alligators**, once threatened, now live mainly in protected southern swamp areas.

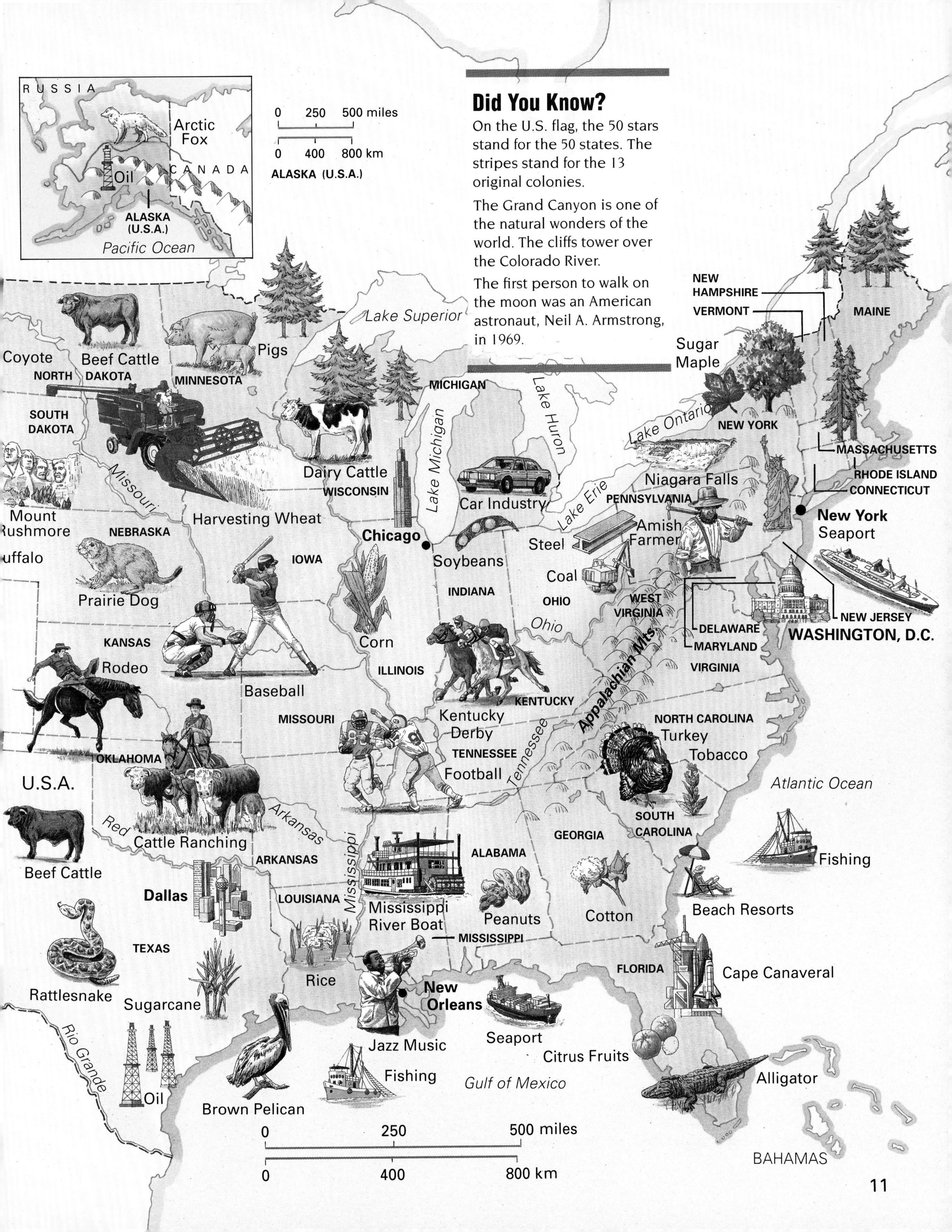
Did You Know?
On the U.S. flag, the 50 stars stand for the 50 states. The stripes stand for the 13 original colonies.
The Grand Canyon is one of the natural wonders of the world. The cliffs tower over the Colorado River.
The first person to walk on the moon was an American astronaut, Neil A. Armstrong, in 1969.
RUSSIA
Arctic Fox
Oil
CANADA
ALASKA (U.S.A.)
Pacific Ocean
0 250 500 miles
0 400 800 km
ALASKA (U.S.A.)
Lake Superior
Coyote
Beef Cattle
NORTH DAKOTA
Pigs
MINNESOTA
SOUTH DAKOTA
Mount Rushmore
Missouri
Harvesting Wheat
Dairy Cattle
WISCONSIN
MICHIGAN
Lake Michigan
Lake Huron
Car Industry
Lake Ontario
Lake Erie
NEW HAMPSHIRE
VERMONT
MAINE
Sugar Maple
NEW YORK
MASSACHUSETTS
RHODE ISLAND
CONNECTICUT
Niagara Falls
PENNSYLVANIA
Amish Farmer
New York Seaport
NEBRASKA
Buffalo
Prairie Dog
IOWA
Chicago
Soybeans
Steel
Coal
INDIANA
OHIO
Ohio
WEST VIRGINIA
NEW JERSEY
DELAWARE
MARYLAND
WASHINGTON, D.C.
KANSAS
Rodeo
Baseball
Corn
ILLINOIS
Appalachian Mts.
VIRGINIA
KENTUCKY
Kentucky Derby
MISSOURI
NORTH CAROLINA
Turkey
Tobacco
TENNESSEE
Tennessee
Football
OKLAHOMA
U.S.A.
Atlantic Ocean
Red
Cattle Ranching
Arkansas
SOUTH CAROLINA
GEORGIA
ALABAMA
Beef Cattle
ARKANSAS
Fishing
Mississippi
Dallas
LOUISIANA
Mississippi River Boat
Peanuts
Cotton
Beach Resorts
MISSISSIPPI
TEXAS
Rice
FLORIDA
Cape Canaveral
Rattlesnake
Sugarcane
New Orleans
Rio Grande
Seaport
Jazz Music
Citrus Fruits
Fishing
Gulf of Mexico
Alligator
Oil
Brown Pelican
0 250 500 miles
0 400 800 km
BAHAMAS

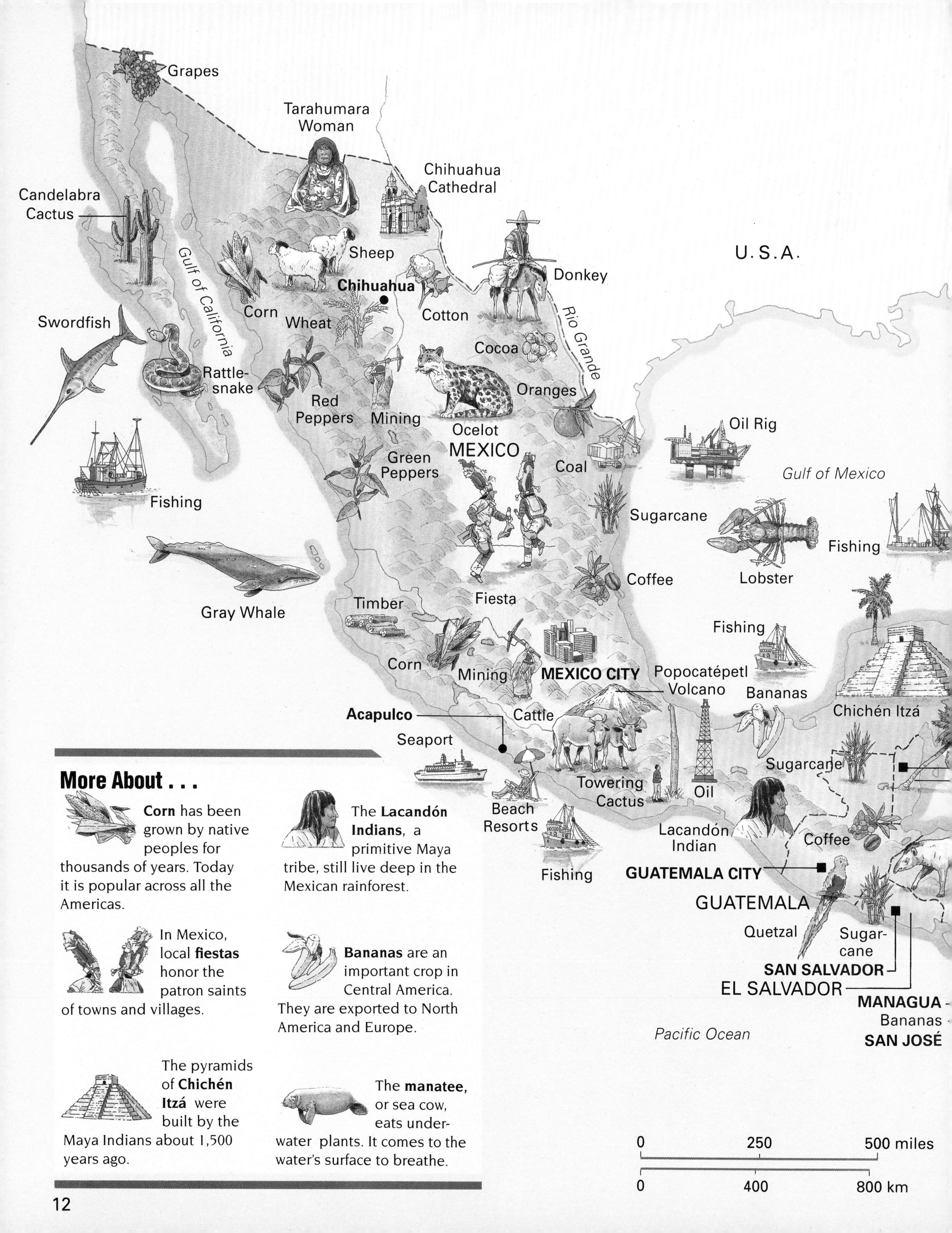

More About . . .

Corn has been grown by native peoples for thousands of years. Today it is popular across all the Americas.

The **Lacandón Indians**, a primitive Maya tribe, still live deep in the Mexican rainforest.

In Mexico, local **fiestas** honor the patron saints of towns and villages.

Bananas are an important crop in Central America. They are exported to North America and Europe.

The pyramids of **Chichén Itzá** were built by the Maya Indians about 1,500 years ago.

The **manatee**, or sea cow, eats under-water plants. It comes to the water's surface to breathe.

Mexico, Central America, and the Caribbean

Mexico is on the North American continent, as are the 7 countries of Central America. These countries form a land bridge between Mexico and South America. People of this area are descendants of the Indians who originally lived here and the Europeans who came more than 400 years ago.

The Caribbean islands stretch in an arc across the Caribbean Sea. These islands were once ruled by other countries, but today most of them are independent. Many Caribbean people are descended from African slaves who were brought to work on the sugar plantations there.

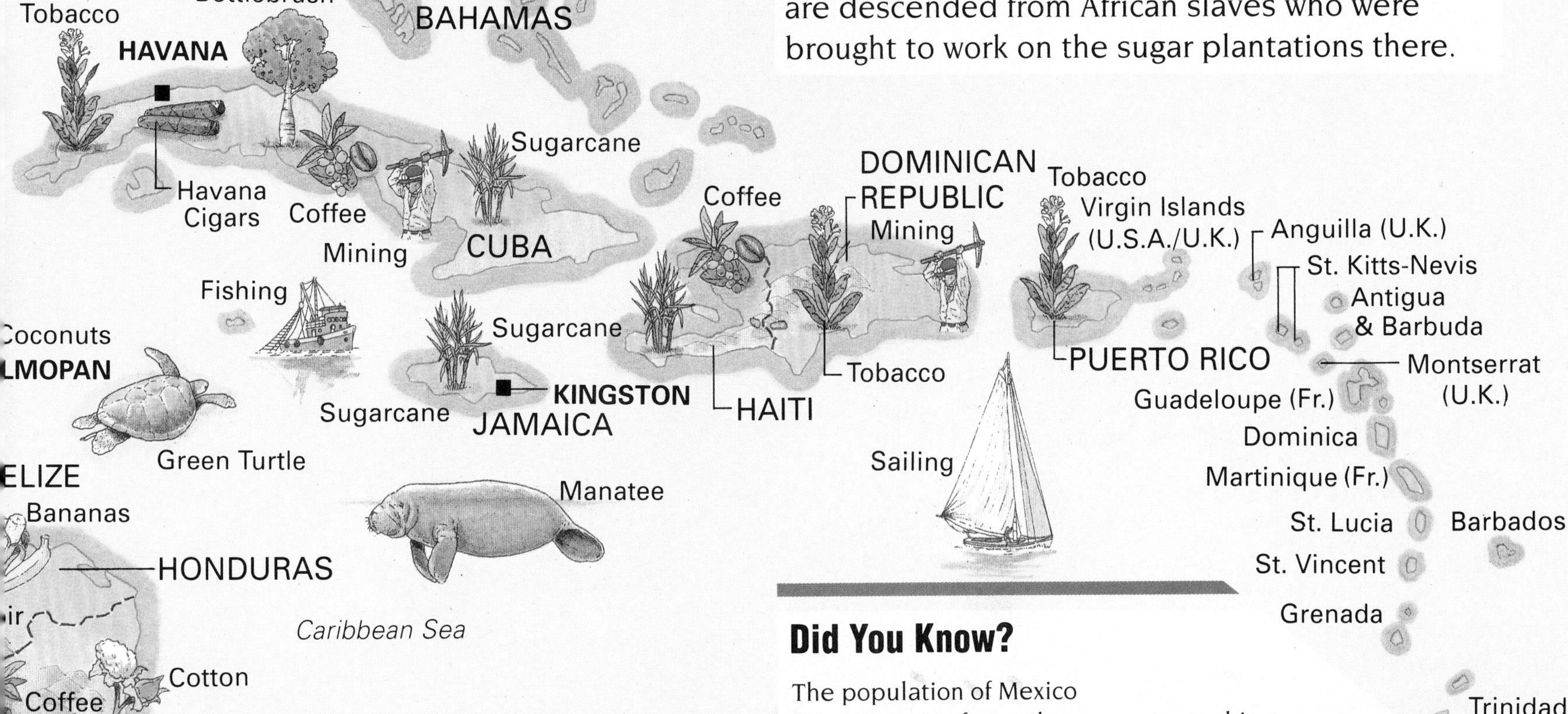

Did You Know?

The population of Mexico City is growing faster than any other city in the world. Twenty million people live there—more than live in the state of Texas. By the year 2000 there will probably be over 30 million.

Mexican children are given a piñata on special occasions. A piñata is a paper animal, filled with candies and toys. It is hung from the ceiling by a string. Blindfolded children try to hit the piñata with a stick to break it open.

The Panama Canal cuts across the country of Panama. It was built to link the Atlantic and Pacific oceans so that ships could avoid going around the tip of South America. It took 10 years to build the canal, which is 51 miles long. It takes a ship 8 hours to pass through the canal.

South America: North

The landscape of this region varies from the high Andes Mountains and desert in the west to thick rainforest in the north and east. The Andes, which run down the west coast of South America, are rich in minerals, such as silver, zinc, and iron. The Amazon River begins high in the mountains of Peru and flows across Brazil. It is fed by hundreds of small rivers in Peru, Bolivia, Ecuador, Colombia, and Venezuela.

Highlands stretch across Venezuela into Guyana, Suriname, and French Guiana. The highlands are mainly rainforest, with small areas of grassland. Venezuela is the richest country in the region. It is one of the world's major oil producers.

The first people to live in South America were Indians. Today South American people are descendants of Indians and of the Europeans who settled there more than 450 years ago.

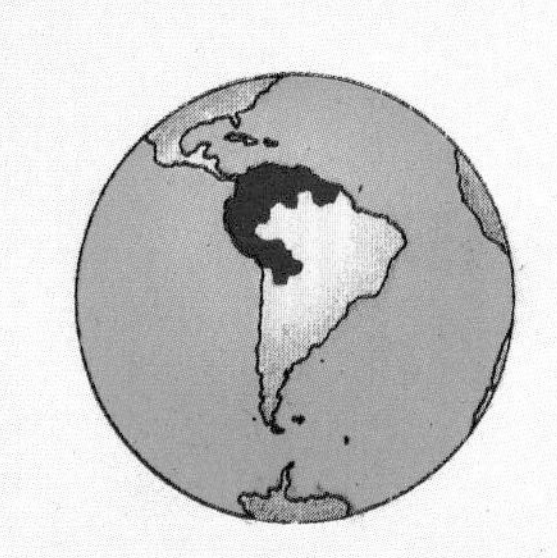

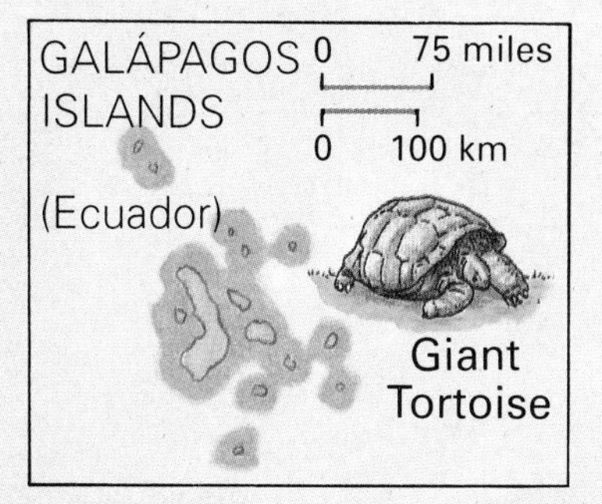

More About . . .

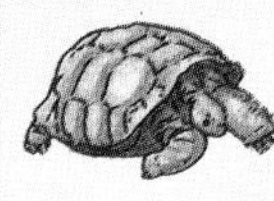

Giant tortoises live on the Galápagos Islands in the Pacific Ocean. They grow up to 5 feet long and can weigh 350 pounds. Today they are an endangered species.

The surviving **Cuiva Indians** live in small groups on the plains of Colombia. Every four weeks they move camp. They hunt wild pigs, catch fish, and gather fruit .

Armadillo means "little armored one" in Spanish. It has hard plates covering its back and sides. This burrowing animal curls up in a ball when it senses danger.

Panama hats are famous all over the world. They are made from leaves of the palmlike jipijapa plant, which grows in Ecuador.

The ruins of the ancient Inca city of **Machu Picchu** were found in 1911. Today it is one of Peru's most popular tourist sites.

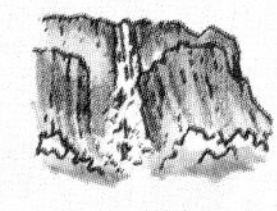

Angel Falls, in Venezuela, is the world's highest waterfall. The water plunges over 3,200 feet into the river below.

The **condor** is a huge bird that is part of the vulture family. The condor soars high over the Andes. Each of its wings is as long as a compact car.

The **Aymara Indians** live high in the Andes Mountains. They fish on Lake Titicaca, using reed boats. The boats are woven from reeds growing on the lakeshore.

Cayenne pepper is bright red and very hot! It is a spice that comes from a plant grown around Cayenne, the capital of French Guiana.

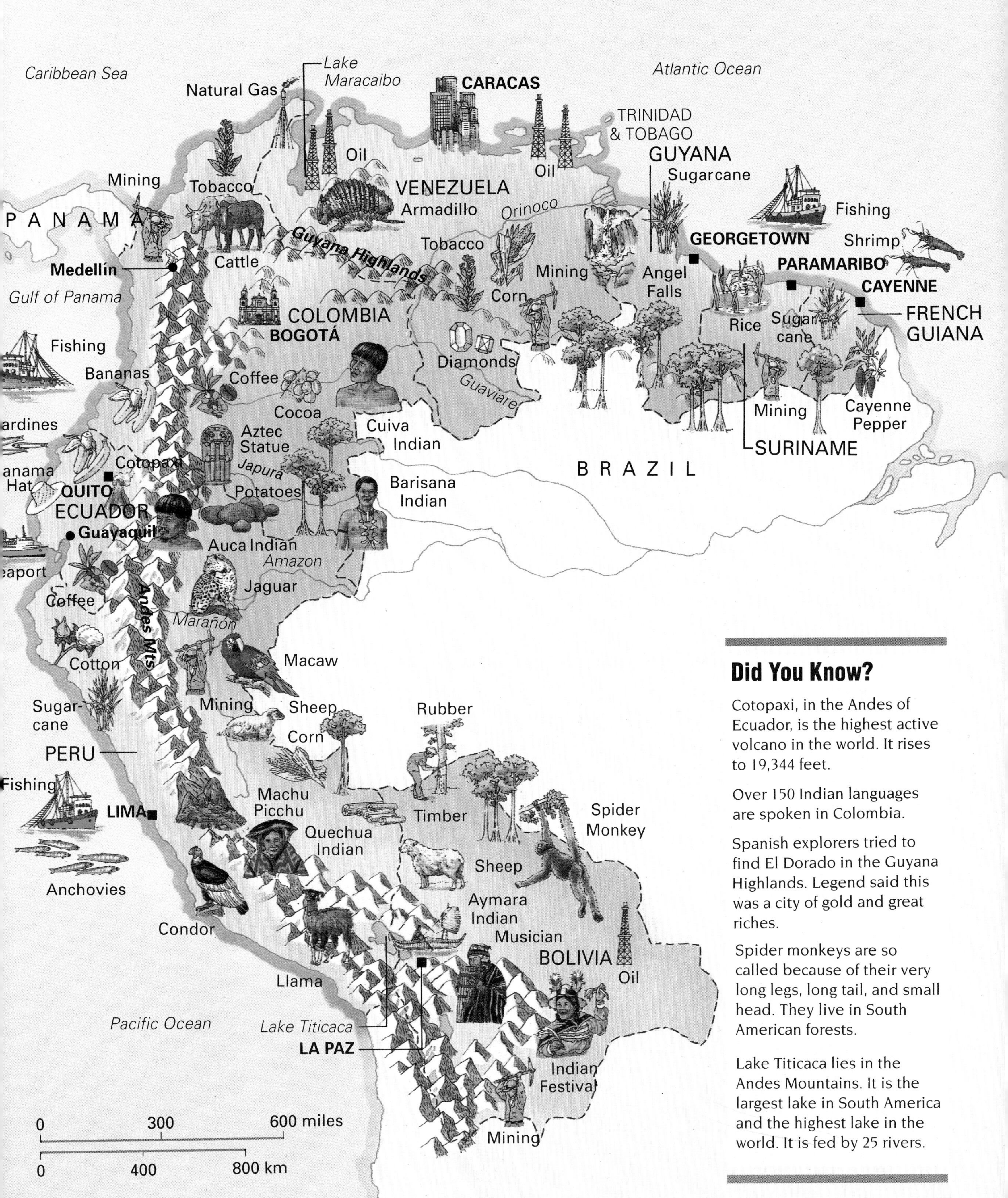

Did You Know?

Cotopaxi, in the Andes of Ecuador, is the highest active volcano in the world. It rises to 19,344 feet.

Over 150 Indian languages are spoken in Colombia.

Spanish explorers tried to find El Dorado in the Guyana Highlands. Legend said this was a city of gold and great riches.

Spider monkeys are so called because of their very long legs, long tail, and small head. They live in South American forests.

Lake Titicaca lies in the Andes Mountains. It is the largest lake in South America and the highest lake in the world. It is fed by 25 rivers.

South America: Brazil

Brazil is the largest country in South America. It contains the biggest tropical rainforest in the world. The Amazon River runs through the hot, steamy terrain. Some Indian tribes still live here.

The main cities of Brazil are in the south of the country. São Paulo is the largest city. Rio de Janeiro, famed for its beaches, is known for its annual carnival. In 1960, the newly built city of Brasília became Brazil's capital.

Did You Know?

So much rain falls in the Amazon region that Brazilians divide the seasons into times of "big rains" and "little rains."

Over 1,000 types of fish live in the Amazon.

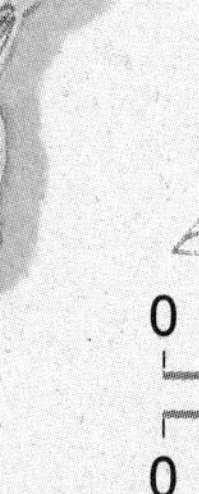

More About . . .

The **carnival** in Rio takes place every year. During this pre-Easter celebration, the streets are alive with music, singing, and dancing.

Much of the **rainforest** is being destroyed. Thousands of plants and animals that live there are becoming extinct.

The **Yanomamo Indians** live in thatched reed houses. They grow crops and hunt monkeys and deer.

South America: South

The Andes Mountains continue south through Chile and Argentina. They stretch to the tip of the South American continent. The Andes dominate Chile, which is a long, narrow country on the Pacific coast. To the east are vast areas of grassland in Argentina, Paraguay, and Uruguay. Cattle and sheep graze here. Wheat and corn grow on the pampas—flat, treeless plains in Argentina. In the south, there are big reserves of oil and gas. The weather is often cold, and there are lakes, waterfalls, and volcanoes.

As in the rest of South America, the people of these countries are descended mainly from Indians and Spanish settlers. Most people live in big cities. The capitals of Argentina, Chile, and Uruguay are each home to over a third of their country's people.

Did You Know?

The Tierra del Fuego islands are shared by two countries. The western islands belong to Chile, and the eastern islands belong to Argentina.

Many interesting animals live in the Andes Mountains. Some of these are llamas, guanacos, alpacas, and vicuñas. They are all members of the camel family.

Penguins live on the southern shores of Chile and Argentina. They also live on the Falkland Islands.

Monkey puzzle trees grow in Chile and Argentina. They got their name because it is said even monkeys find them hard to climb.

More About . . .

The **prickly pear cactus** grows in the deserts of North and South America. It bears a pearlike fruit covered in thorns.

Gauchos are Argentinian cowboys. They herd cattle on the grassy plains called pampas.

Soccer is the national sport in South America. Argentina and Uruguay have each won the World Cup twice.

The **Andes** form the longest mountain chain in the world —stretching for 4,600 miles.

North Europe

The British Isles consists of the large islands of Great Britain (England, Scotland, Wales) and Ireland, plus many smaller islands. The United Kingdom is a country made up of Great Britain and Northern Ireland. The southern part of Ireland (the Republic of Ireland) is an independent country. Cows and sheep graze on pastures all over the British Isles. Oil and gas are found in the North Sea off Scotland.

Norway, Sweden, Denmark, Finland, and Iceland make up Scandinavia. Huge forests in Scandinavia provide wood to make paper and furniture. These countries also have large fishing fleets.

Greenland, a part of Denmark, is a very large island. Most of it lies within the Arctic Circle. Few people live there.

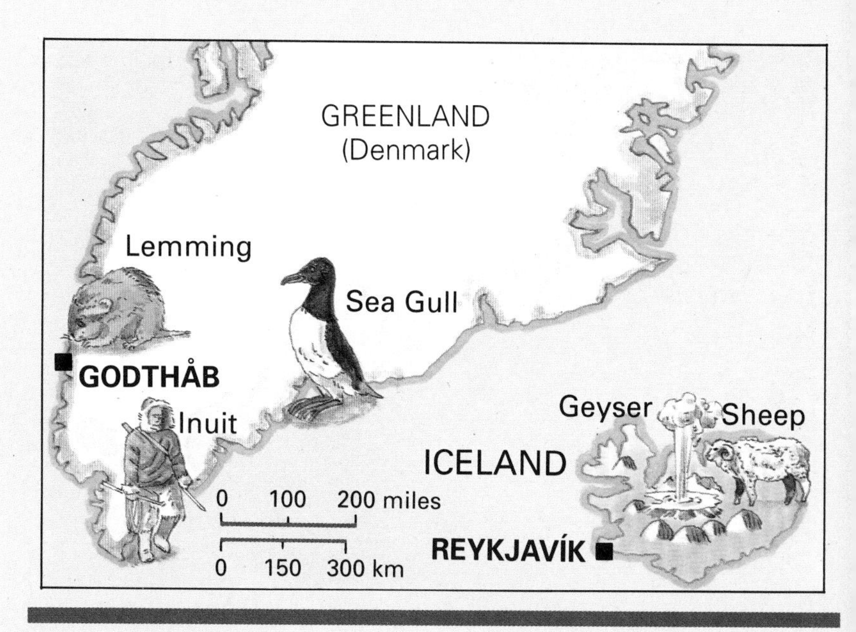

More About . . .

Hot **geysers** spring up from beneath the frozen earth in Iceland.

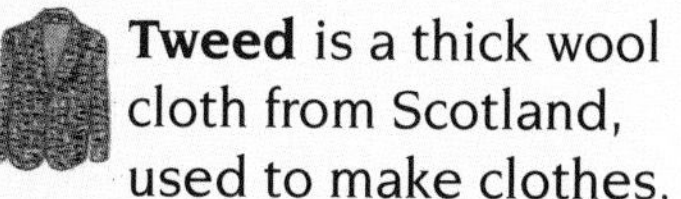

Tweed is a thick wool cloth from Scotland, used to make clothes.

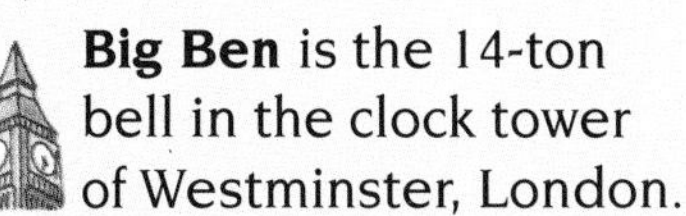

Big Ben is the 14-ton bell in the clock tower of Westminster, London.

Hadrian's Wall was built by the ancient Romans for protection.

Did You Know?

There are about 60,000 lakes in Finland.

At Legoland in the Danish town of Billund, 38 million Lego bricks are used to make model statues, buildings, and animals.

Norway is more than twice as large as England, but England has over 10 times as many people.

More About . . .

Cross-country skiing is popular in the snowy countries of Scandinavia.

A **sauna** is a steam bath. Finnish people often take a dip in the snow after a sauna!

The **Little Mermaid** statue is perched on rocks off the harbor of Copenhagen, Denmark.

Norwegian **stave churches** are made of wood and were built more than 700 years ago.

France and the **Low Countries**

France is the largest country in western Europe. It has rich farmlands, and its mild climate is ideal for growing wheat, corn, and barley. Grapes also grow here, and French wine is the most famous in the world. France is also well known for its fine food, in restaurants and in the home.

There are many beautiful French cities. Paris, the capital, is an important center of art and learning. The main industrial region lies north of Paris. The Alps, in the south of France, are popular for skiing. The Riviera, along the Mediterranean coast, is a region with many beach resorts.

The Low Countries consist of Belgium, the Netherlands (Holland), and Luxembourg. Much of the Netherlands is below sea level. However, the Dutch people have built special dams called dikes to hold back the sea.

More About . . .

Truffles are mushroomlike plants that grow underground and have a special taste. Pigs and dogs are used for truffle hunting.

In the Netherlands, **windmills** are no longer used to pump floodwater from the land. Dikes have been built to keep the land dry.

The **Tour de France** is the best-known bicycle race in the world. Cyclists from many countries compete in it. The route covers 2,200 miles and finishes in Paris.

TGV high-speed trains run from Paris to other French cities. They are the fastest passenger trains in the world.

Basque shepherds live in the foothills of the Pyrenees. The Basques speak their own language. Some Basques want their own state.

The **cave paintings** at Lascaux may be 17,000 years old. They show horses, deer, and other animals. Tourists flock to Lascaux.

Did You Know?

Luxembourg has more than 100 castles, and many are partly in ruins. It has been called the "Land of Haunted Castles."

France, Belgium, the Netherlands, and Luxembourg are all in the European Community. Its headquarters is in Brussels, Belgium's capital. The Community brings member countries closer together and helps them do business with each other. Other members are Denmark, Germany, Greece, Ireland, Italy, Portugal, Spain, and the U.K.

Belgium has two groups of native people. Flemings speak Flemish, a form of Dutch, and Walloons speak a French dialect.

The city of Amsterdam, in the Netherlands, is built on about 100 islands, which are joined by a series of canals. At least 50 cars a year fall into the canals. There are special police to recover sunken cars and bikes.

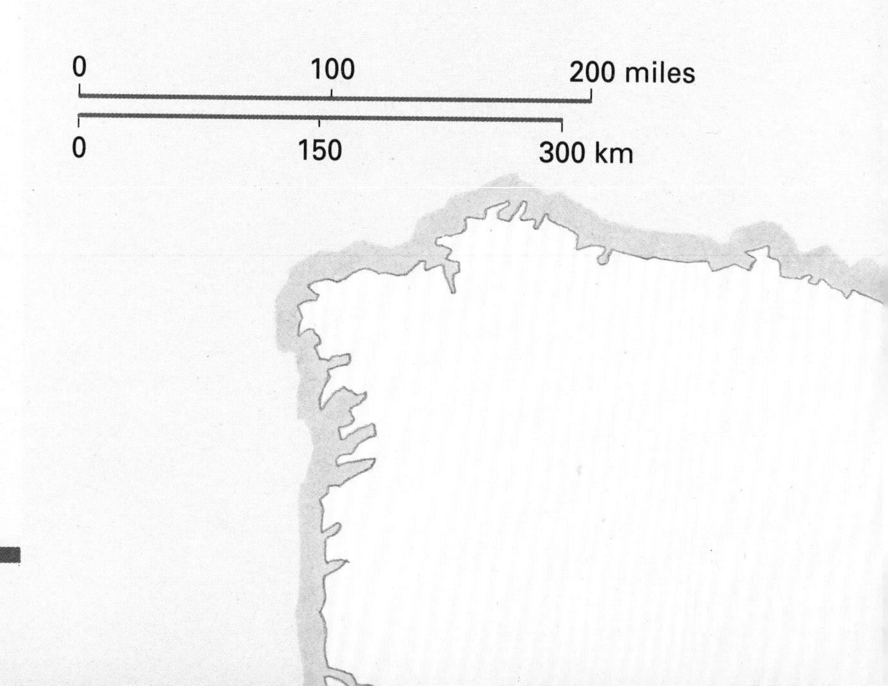

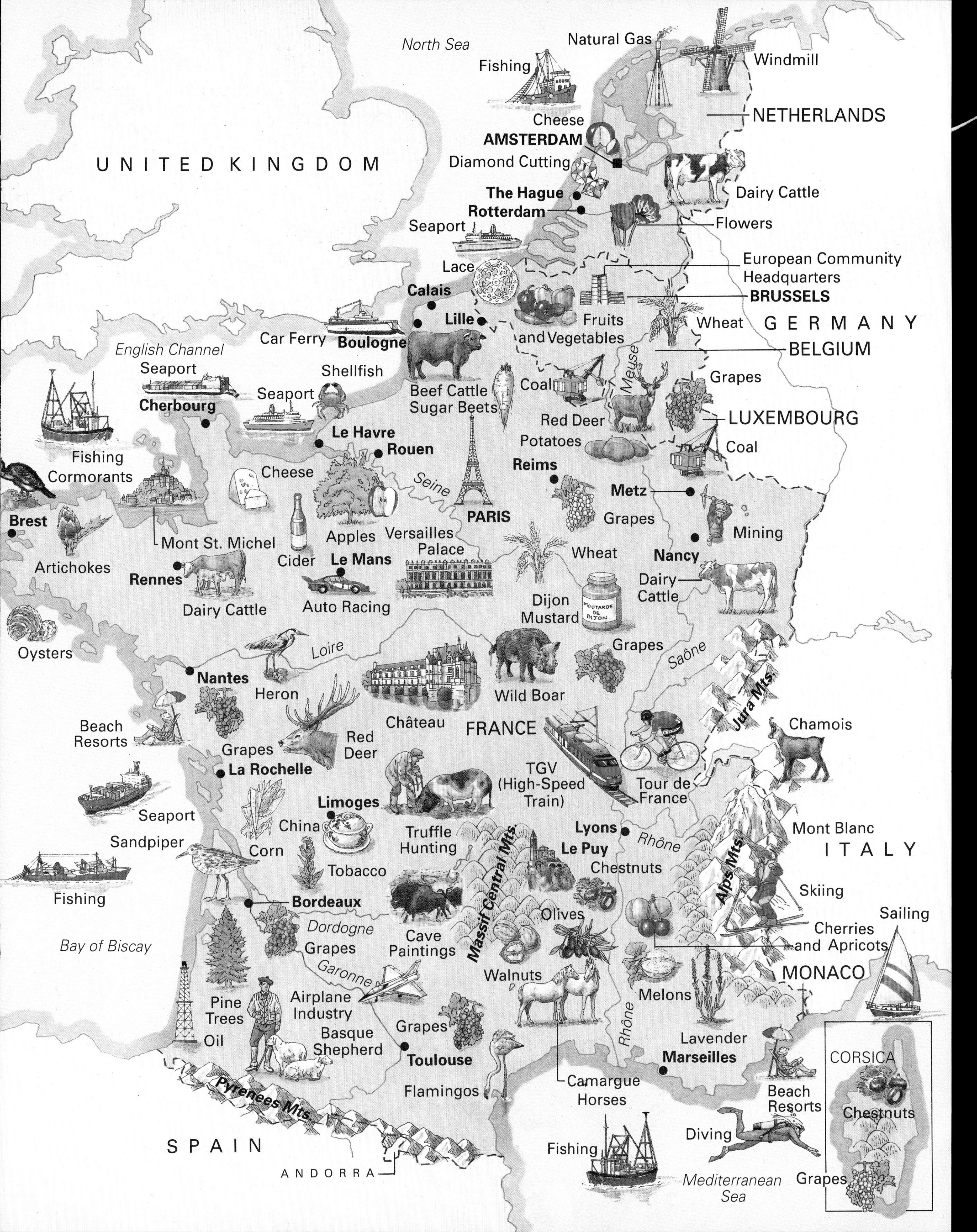

North Sea
Natural Gas
Fishing
Windmill
NETHERLANDS
Cheese
AMSTERDAM
Diamond Cutting
UNITED KINGDOM
Dairy Cattle
The Hague
Rotterdam
Flowers
Seaport
European Community Headquarters
Lace
Calais
BRUSSELS
Lille
Fruits and Vegetables
Wheat
GERMANY
Car Ferry
Boulogne
BELGIUM
English Channel
Seaport
Shellfish
Meuse
Grapes
Seaport
Coal
Cherbourg
Beef Cattle
Sugar Beets
LUXEMBOURG
Red Deer
Le Havre
Potatoes
Coal
Rouen
Fishing
Cormorants
Reims
Cheese
Seine
Metz
Brest
PARIS
Grapes
Mining
Mont St. Michel
Apples
Versailles Palace
Wheat
Nancy
Artichokes
Cider
Le Mans
Rennes
Dairy Cattle
Dijon Mustard
MOUTARDE DE DIJON
Auto Racing
Dairy Cattle
Oysters
Loire
Grapes
Saône
Nantes
Heron
Wild Boar
Beach Resorts
Château
Jura Mts.
Chamois
FRANCE
Grapes
Red Deer
La Rochelle
TGV (High-Speed Train)
Tour de France
Seaport
Limoges
China
Truffle Hunting
Lyons
Mont Blanc
Sandpiper
Le Puy
Rhône
ITALY
Corn
Massif Central Mts.
Chestnuts
Alps Mts.
Tobacco
Skiing
Fishing
Bordeaux
Olives
Sailing
Dordogne
Cherries and Apricots
Bay of Biscay
Grapes
Cave Paintings
MONACO
Garonne
Walnuts
Melons
Pine Trees
Airplane Industry
Rhône
Oil
Basque Shepherd
Grapes
Lavender
CORSICA
Toulouse
Marseilles
Pyrenees Mts.
Flamingos
Camargue Horses
Beach Resorts
Chestnuts
SPAIN
Diving
Fishing
ANDORRA
Mediterranean Sea
Grapes

Central Europe

Central Europe is dominated by Germany, a leading industrial nation. The Ruhr valley is a region of heavy industry, and the Rhine River is an important route for transporting cargo. Northern Germany has plains with fertile farmlands. Southern Germany has mountains and forests. Farther south are the countries of Switzerland and Austria. They are dominated by the mountains of the Alps.

To the east lie the Czech Republic, Slovakia, and Poland. They are rich in natural resources and have large industries. Poland has steel and shipbuilding centers on the Baltic Sea. Farming is also important in these countries.

More About . . .

Neuschwanstein castle in Bavaria was built over 100 years ago for King Ludwig II.

Switzerland is famous for its watchmaking. Swiss **watches** and clocks are popular all over the world.

Bohemia is a region of the Czech Republic that is popular with tourists. **Bohemian glassware** is made there.

The **chamois** is a wild antelope the size of a goat. It lives in the mountains and eats herbs, flowers, and pine shoots.

Bison were once found throughout Europe. Now only a few are left. Most live in a protected forest in Poland.

Lipizzaner horses are trained at the Spanish Riding School in Vienna, Austria. They put on impressive shows at home and abroad.

0 75 150 miles

0 100 200 km

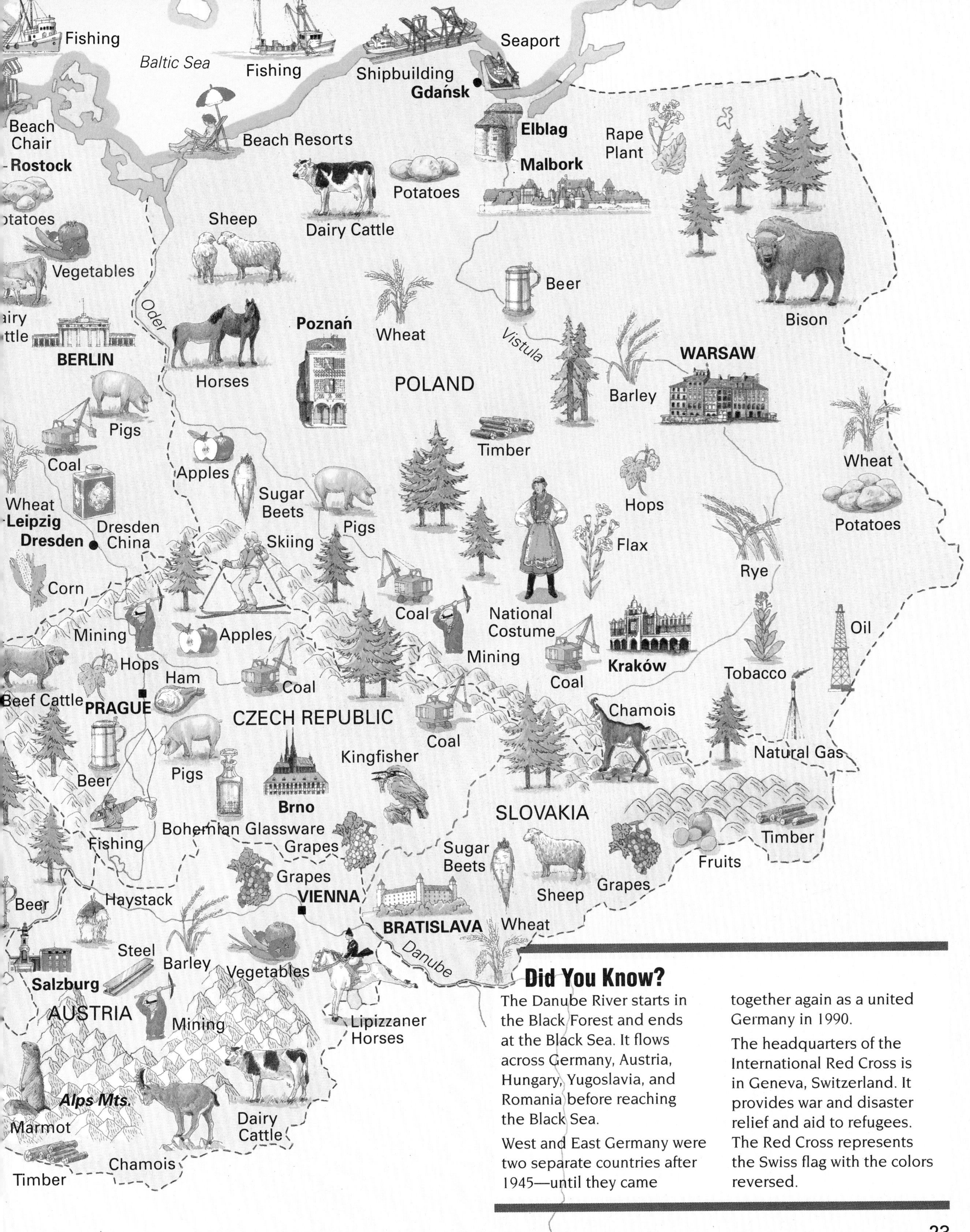

Did You Know?

The Danube River starts in the Black Forest and ends at the Black Sea. It flows across Germany, Austria, Hungary, Yugoslavia, and Romania before reaching the Black Sea.

West and East Germany were two separate countries after 1945—until they came together again as a united Germany in 1990.

The headquarters of the International Red Cross is in Geneva, Switzerland. It provides war and disaster relief and aid to refugees. The Red Cross represents the Swiss flag with the colors reversed.

Spain, Portugal, and Italy

Several mountain ranges cross Spain. The highest mountains are the Pyrenees, between Spain and France, and the Sierra Nevada in the south. Many Spaniards now live and work in the towns, but others still work on the land, growing olives, citrus fruits, and grapes. Portugal, to the west of Spain, is a much smaller country. Many Portuguese are fishermen or farmers.

Italy is a long, narrow country, with the Apennine Mountains running through its center. In the north there are factories where cars and textiles are made. In the south farmers grow fruits, such as olives and oranges.

The climate in Spain, Portugal, and Italy is mild. The region's beaches are popular vacation spots.

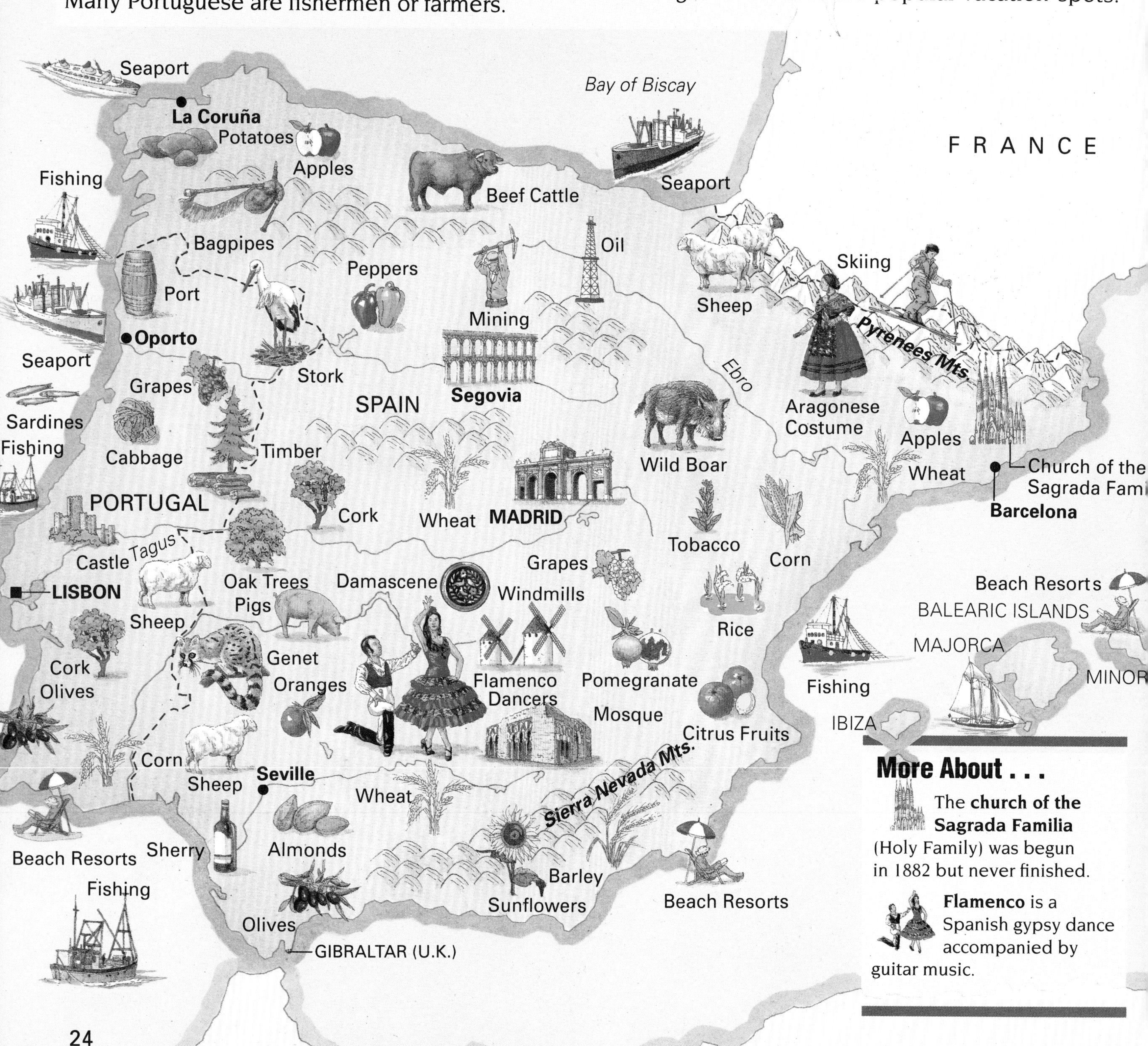

More About . . .

The **church of the Sagrada Familia** (Holy Family) was begun in 1882 but never finished.

Flamenco is a Spanish gypsy dance accompanied by guitar music.

More About . . .

Cork is the bark of an oak tree used to make bottle stoppers.

In A.D. 79, Mount Vesuvius erupted. Volcanic ash buried the city of **Pompeii.**

Pasta is a popular food in Italy. It is traditionally made from wheat flour and water.

People who visit Venice can travel along its canals in boats called **gondolas.**

Toledo, Spain, is famous for **damascene**—black metals inlaid with gold and silver thread.

Saint Francis was born in **Assisi,** Italy. He gave up his wealth to live as a monk.

Did You Know?

The Vatican City is an independent state within the city of Rome. The Pope, head of the Roman Catholic Church, lives here. The Vatican City is also the smallest country in the world, with its own banking, telephone, and postal systems.

On Sunday afternoons in Spain, large crowds gather to watch bullfights. The matador, in his sequined suit, flicks his bright-colored cape at the charging bull and tries to avoid the bull's sharp horns.

Portugal is famous for port, a dark, strong red wine.

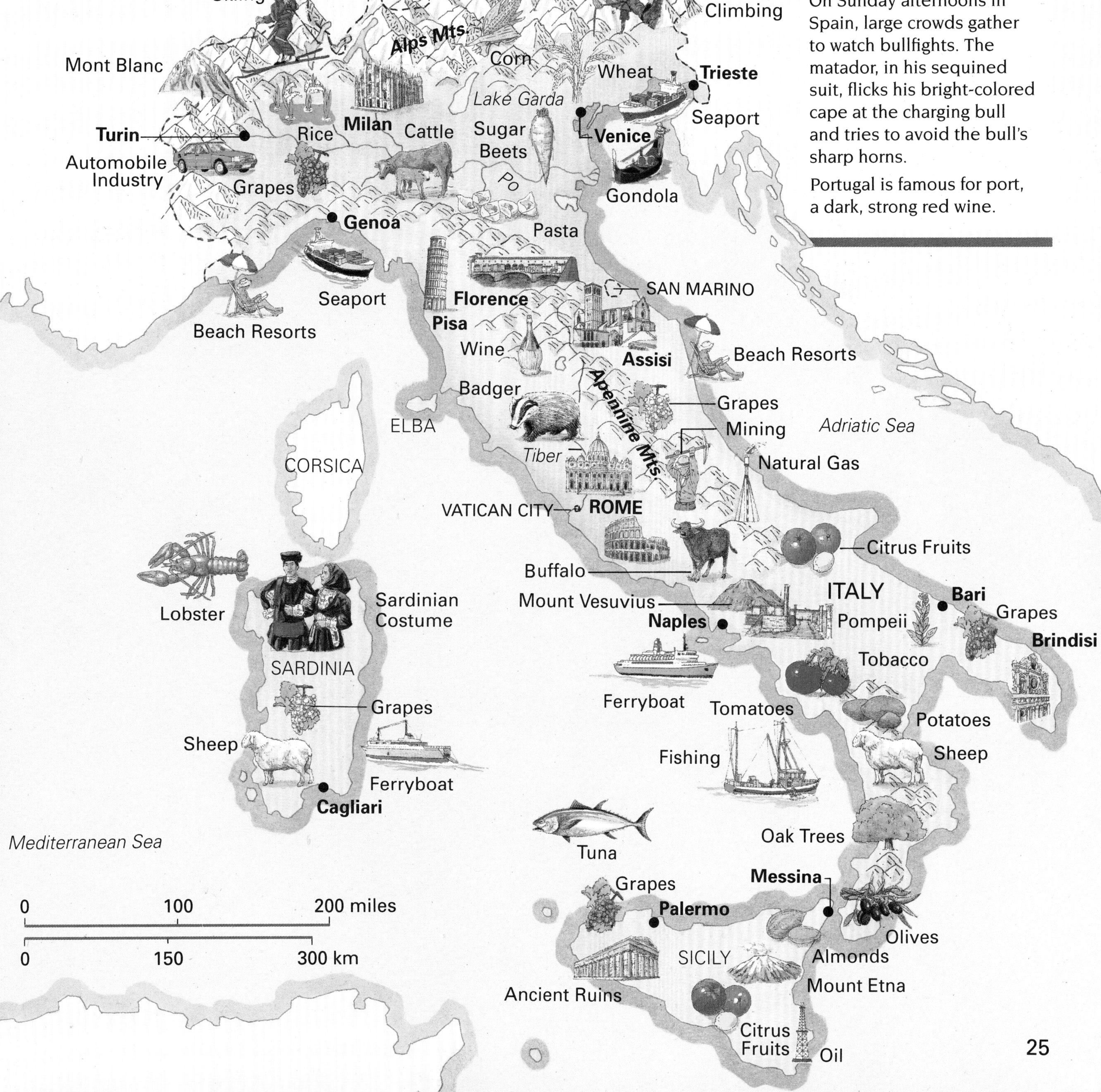

Southeast Europe

Hungary, Serbia, Croatia, Romania, Bulgaria, and Greece are all part of southeast Europe. Budapest, the capital of Hungary, lies on the banks of the Danube River, which flows south into Serbia—one of the 6 separate republics that formerly made up the country of Yugoslavia. Differences between the 2 largest republics, Serbia and Croatia, led to civil war in 1991.

The Danube continues its journey to the Black Sea, forming the border between Romania and Bulgaria. Both countries have high mountain ranges: the Carpathians and the Transylvanian Alps in Romania; the Balkans in Bulgaria.

Albania is a small, poor country on the Adriatic Sea. To the south is the mainland of Greece, with its many islands. Tourism is very important to Greece. People come to visit the ancient ruins and to enjoy the country's islands and beaches.

Did You Know?

The ancient Olympic Games were first held at Olympia, Greece, in 776 B.C. The first modern Olympics were held in Athens in 1896.

Count Dracula, the infamous vampire, is supposed to have come from Transylvania, a region of Romania.

Skopje, the capital of the Yugoslav republic of Macedonia, has had a difficult history. In 1689 it was burned down to stop the spread of cholera disease, and in 1963 it was almost destroyed by an earthquake.

Just over 3 million people live in the city of Athens—almost as many people as in the whole country of Albania.

More About . . .

The **Parthenon** temple in Athens is more than 2,400 years old. It was built in honor of the goddess Athena.

The **Golden Kine** (or cows) are part of a gold treasure found in Bulgaria. It may be more than 6,000 years old!

Pelicans live around the Black Sea. This large bird uses the pouch attached to its bill to scoop up fish from the water.

Bran Castle was built in 1377 to guard a pass over the Transylvanian Alps.

The **Valley of Roses** is a famous rose-growing area in Bulgaria. It also produces a rose oil used in perfumes.

Olives are the fruit of the olive tree. They are green when unripe and black when ripe.

Csikós are Hungarian cowboys who once worked on the Great Hungarian Plain. Today most perform in shows for tourists.

The Romans built a vast **amphitheater,** seating thousands, at the port of Pula in Croatia.

Dinaric Alps Mts.

Fishing

Split

Adriatic Sea

ITALY

0 100 200 miles

0 150 300 km

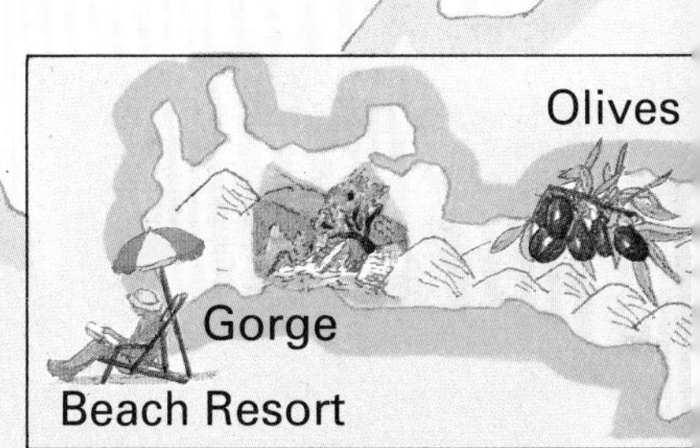

UKRAINE
Timber
Coal
Lynx
Sugar Beets
Grapes
Rice
Apples
BUDAPEST
Csikós
Grapes
Mining
Stork
MOLDAVIA
Corn
Pigs
HUNGARY
Danube
Wheat
Cluj-Napoca
Carpathian Mts.
Monastery
Sugar Beets
Beef Cattle
Wild Boar
Sunflowers
Potatoes
Corn
Grapes
Natural Gas
Drava
Paprika
Transylvanian Alps Mts.
Pelican
Apples
Bran Castle
Natural Gas
CROATIA
Dairy Cattle
Timber
Wheat
Pigs
Pigs
Coal
Reeds
BOSNIA AND HERZEGOVINA
BELGRADE
Geese
Tobacco
ROMANIA
Skiing
Wheat
Grapes
Mining
Potatoes
BUCHAREST
Mining
Oil
Grapes
SARAJEVO
Mining
Corn
Danube
Beach Resorts
SERBIA
Sugar Beets
Brown Bear
Wheat
Wheat
Sunflowers
BULGARIA
Roses
Golden Kine
Beach Resorts
MONTENEGRO
Black Sea
Grapes
Dubrovnik
SOFIA
Coal
Balkan Mts.
Barley
Timber
Grapes
Sheep
SKOPJE
MACEDONIA
Timber
Tobacco
Cotton
Goat
Sheep
Fishing
Cattle
Cotton
TIRANË
Greek Dancers
Tobacco
ALBANIA
Pindus Mts.
Grapes
Olives
Mount Olympus
CORFU
Aegean Sea
Figs
Citrus Fruits
Sheep
TURKEY
Ionian Sea
GREECE
The Parthenon
Fishing
Olives
Octopus
Windmills
Corinth
ATHENS
0
50 miles
0
75 km
Mining
Beach Resorts
Seaport
Beach Resorts
CRETE
Palm Tree
Olympia Ruins
Silver
Ancient Ruins
RHODES

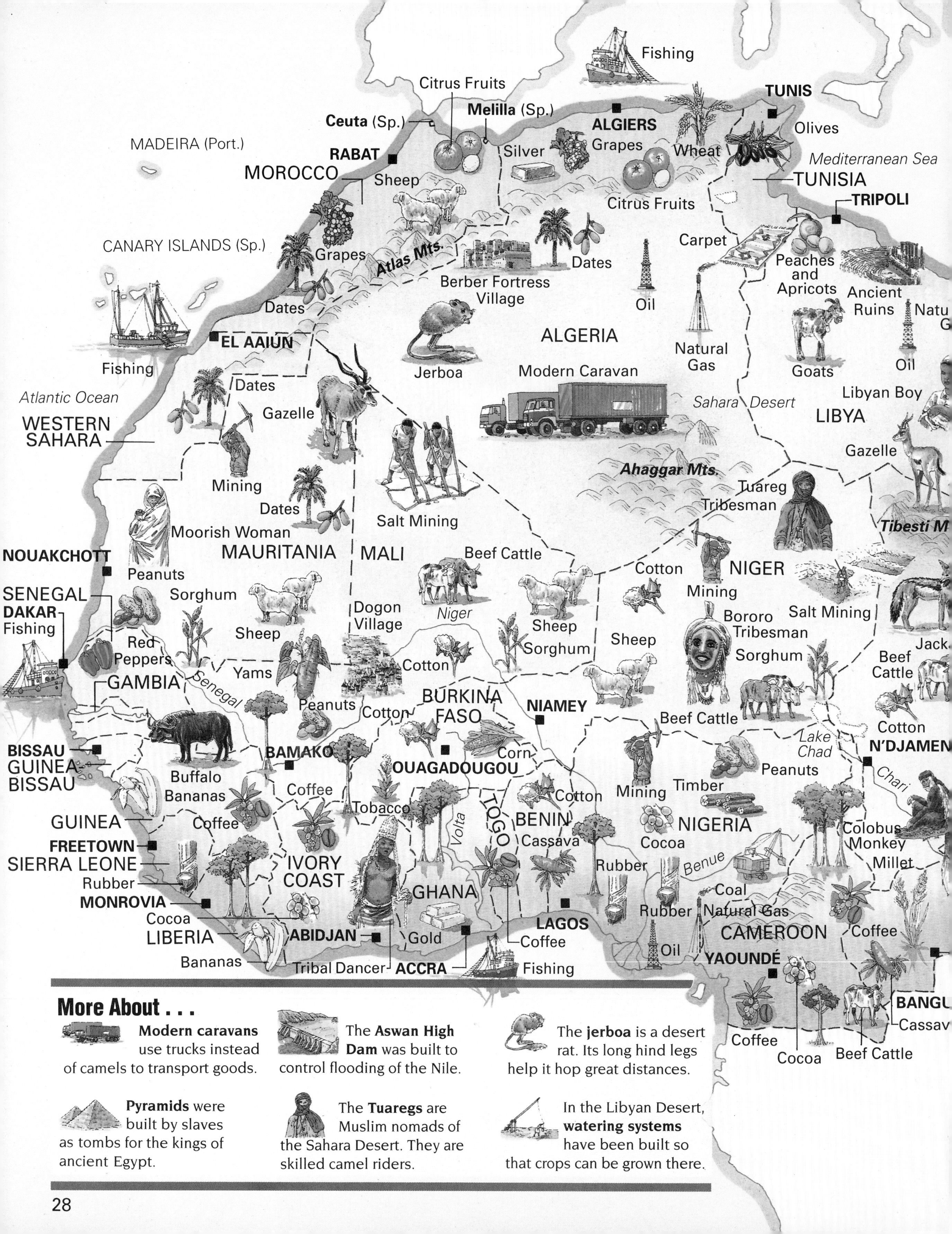

More About . . .

Modern caravans use trucks instead of camels to transport goods.

The **Aswan High Dam** was built to control flooding of the Nile.

The **jerboa** is a desert rat. Its long hind legs help it hop great distances.

Pyramids were built by slaves as tombs for the kings of ancient Egypt.

The **Tuaregs** are Muslim nomads of the Sahara Desert. They are skilled camel riders.

In the Libyan Desert, **watering systems** have been built so that crops can be grown there.

Africa: North

The vast Sahara Desert stretches across north Africa. It is the largest desert in the world and covers all or part of 12 countries. Egypt is located on the east coast of Africa. Most Egyptians live on the 10-mile-wide oasis of the Nile River between Aswan and Cairo and in the delta below Cairo. The Nile flows from central Africa to the Mediterranean Sea. The river's name changes from country to country. The Blue Nile begins on the highlands of Ethiopia, joining the White Nile in Sudan. In both Sudan and Ethiopia, lack of rain and crop failures have caused terrible shortages of food, or famines.

On the west coast of Africa, the situation is different. In Nigeria, oil production started in the 1950s, and the money has been used to build roads, schools, and hospitals. The coast of Cameroon, which borders Nigeria, is a swamp. The southern part of Cameroon is a rainforest.

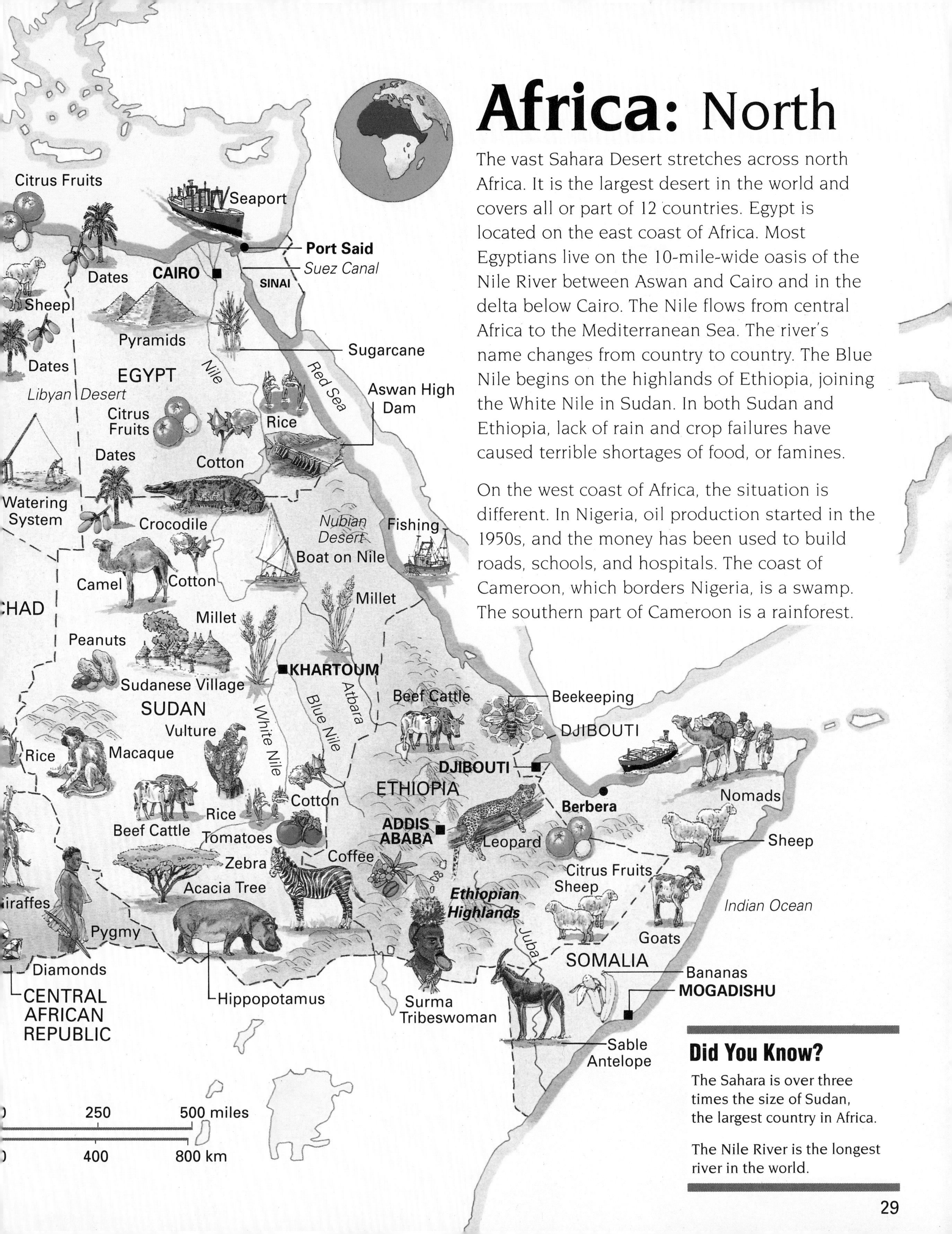

Did You Know?

The Sahara is over three times the size of Sudan, the largest country in Africa.

The Nile River is the longest river in the world.

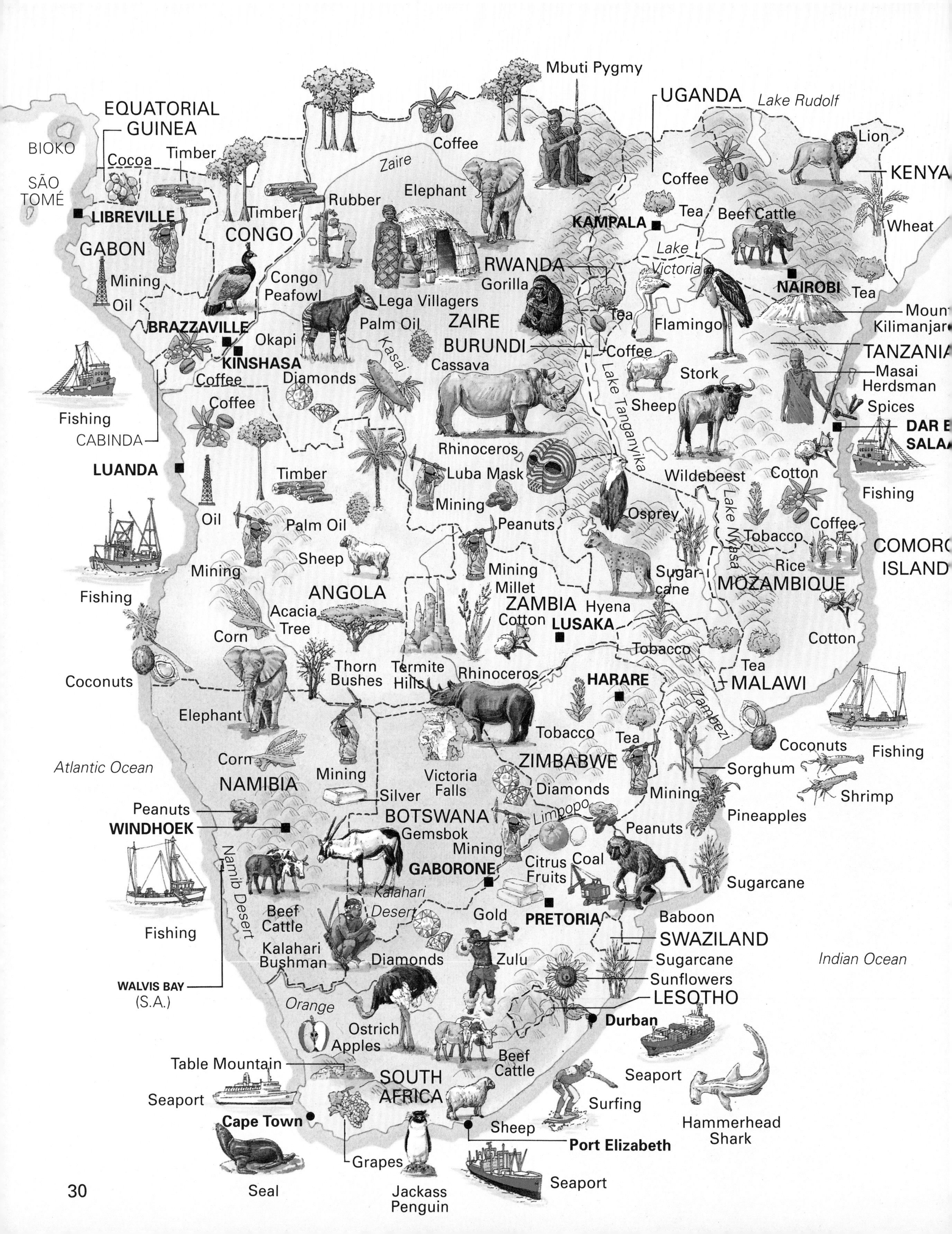

EQUATORIAL GUINEA
BIOKO
SÃO TOMÉ
Cocoa
Timber
Coffee
Zaire
Mbuti Pygmy
UGANDA
Lake Rudolf
Lion
KENYA
LIBREVILLE
GABON
Timber
CONGO
Rubber
Elephant
Coffee
KAMPALA
Tea
Beef Cattle
Wheat
Mining
Oil
Congo Peafowl
Lega Villagers
RWANDA
Gorilla
Lake Victoria
NAIROBI
Tea
Mount Kilimanjaro
BRAZZAVILLE
KINSHASA
Okapi
Palm Oil
ZAIRE
Kasai
BURUNDI
Tea
Coffee
Flamingo
TANZANIA
Coffee
Diamonds
Cassava
Lake Tanganyika
Stork
Masai Herdsman
Fishing
Coffee
Sheep
Spices
CABINDA
Rhinoceros
DAR ES SALAAM
LUANDA
Timber
Luba Mask
Wildebeest
Cotton
Fishing
Oil
Mining
Osprey
Coffee
Palm Oil
Peanuts
Lake Nyasa
Tobacco
COMOROS ISLANDS
Sheep
Mining
Rice
Mining
Millet
Sugar-cane
MOZAMBIQUE
ANGOLA
ZAMBIA
Hyena
Fishing
Acacia Tree
Cotton
LUSAKA
Corn
Tobacco
Cotton
Thorn Bushes
Termite Hills
Rhinoceros
Tea
Coconuts
HARARE
MALAWI
Zambezi
Elephant
Tobacco
Tea
Corn
Mining
Coconuts
Fishing
Atlantic Ocean
ZIMBABWE
Sorghum
Victoria Falls
Shrimp
NAMIBIA
Diamonds
Mining
Silver
Limpopo
Peanuts
BOTSWANA
Pineapples
WINDHOEK
Gemsbok
Peanuts
Mining
Citrus Fruits
Coal
GABORONE
Sugarcane
Kalahari Desert
Namib Desert
Beef Cattle
Gold
PRETORIA
Baboon
Fishing
SWAZILAND
Kalahari Bushman
Diamonds
Zulu
Sugarcane
Indian Ocean
Sunflowers
WALVIS BAY (S.A.)
LESOTHO
Orange
Durban
Ostrich
Apples
Beef Cattle
Seaport
Table Mountain
SOUTH AFRICA
Surfing
Seaport
Hammerhead Shark
Cape Town
Sheep
Port Elizabeth
Grapes
Seaport
Seal
Jackass Penguin

Africa: South

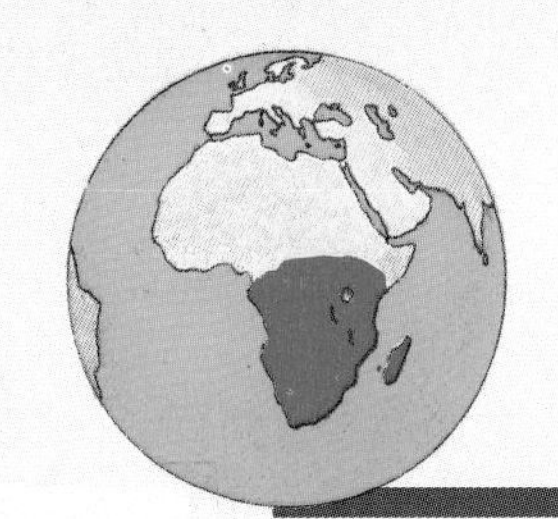

Tropical rainforests are found across south Africa. The Zaire River, also called the Congo, flows through the country of Zaire on its journey to the Atlantic Ocean. To the east, Kenya and Tanzania are famous for their wildlife. Antelopes, zebras, giraffes, elephants, and rhinoceroses live on the savanna, a flat grassland. Snowcapped Mount Kilimanjaro, in Tanzania, isAfrica's highest mountain. Farther south are the Kalahari Desert and the smaller Namib Desert.

Most southern African countries are rich in minerals. Zimbabwe has large deposits of copper, iron, and gold. In South Africa, coal and diamonds are mined. The largest white population on the continent is found in South Africa. In 1994 white minority rule in that country gave way to a democratically elected, coalition government headed by a black president, Nelson Mandela, son of a Thembu chief.

The island of Madagascar lies in the Indian Ocean. Most of its people are farmers.

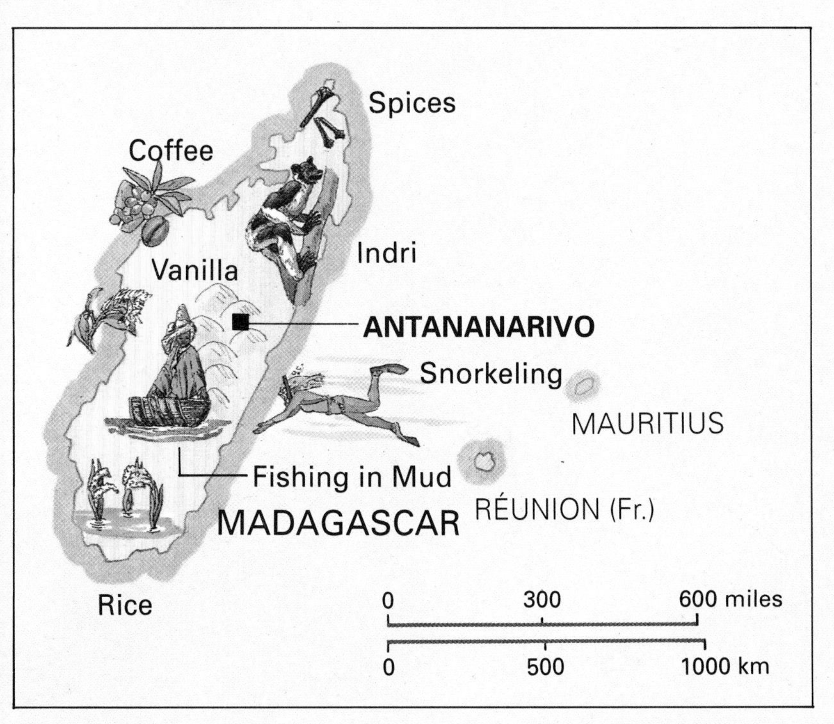

More About . . .

The **Mbuti pygmies** of Zaire are the smallest people in the world. Their average height is 4 feet, 6 inches.

Gorillas live in some African rainforests. They look fierce, but are not dangerous unless attacked.

Miners blast or dig out rocks containing **diamonds**. The gems are then separated from gravel and other rock fragments.

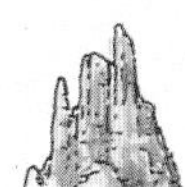

Like bees, termites live in groups called colonies. **Termite hills** are the giant nests that termite colonies make from mounds of earth.

The **Kalahari bushmen** roam the desert. The women collect roots and berries, while the men hunt.

Zulus are the largest group of black Africans in South Africa. Many now work in the cities.

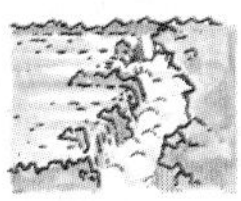

The spectacular **Victoria Falls,** of the Zambesi River, plunge 350 feet into a giant gorge below.

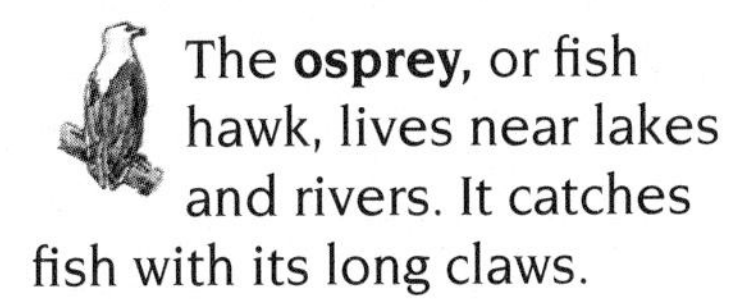

The **osprey,** or fish hawk, lives near lakes and rivers. It catches fish with its long claws.

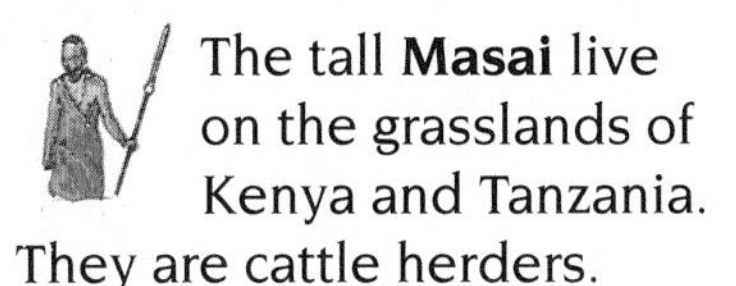

The tall **Masai** live on the grasslands of Kenya and Tanzania. They are cattle herders.

The **rhinoceros** is usually calm. However, when it is threatened, the rhinoceros can charge at 31 miles per hour.

Did You Know?

The Watusi live in Rwanda and Burundi. They are among the tallest people in the world. The average height for men is 6 feet, 5 inches.

In 1867, children playing beside the Orange River found the first South African diamond. A few years later there was a diamond rush, and the world-famous Kimberley mines opened.

Diamonds are harder than any other natural substance. Many are used in industry as parts of cutting tools.

Former Soviet Union

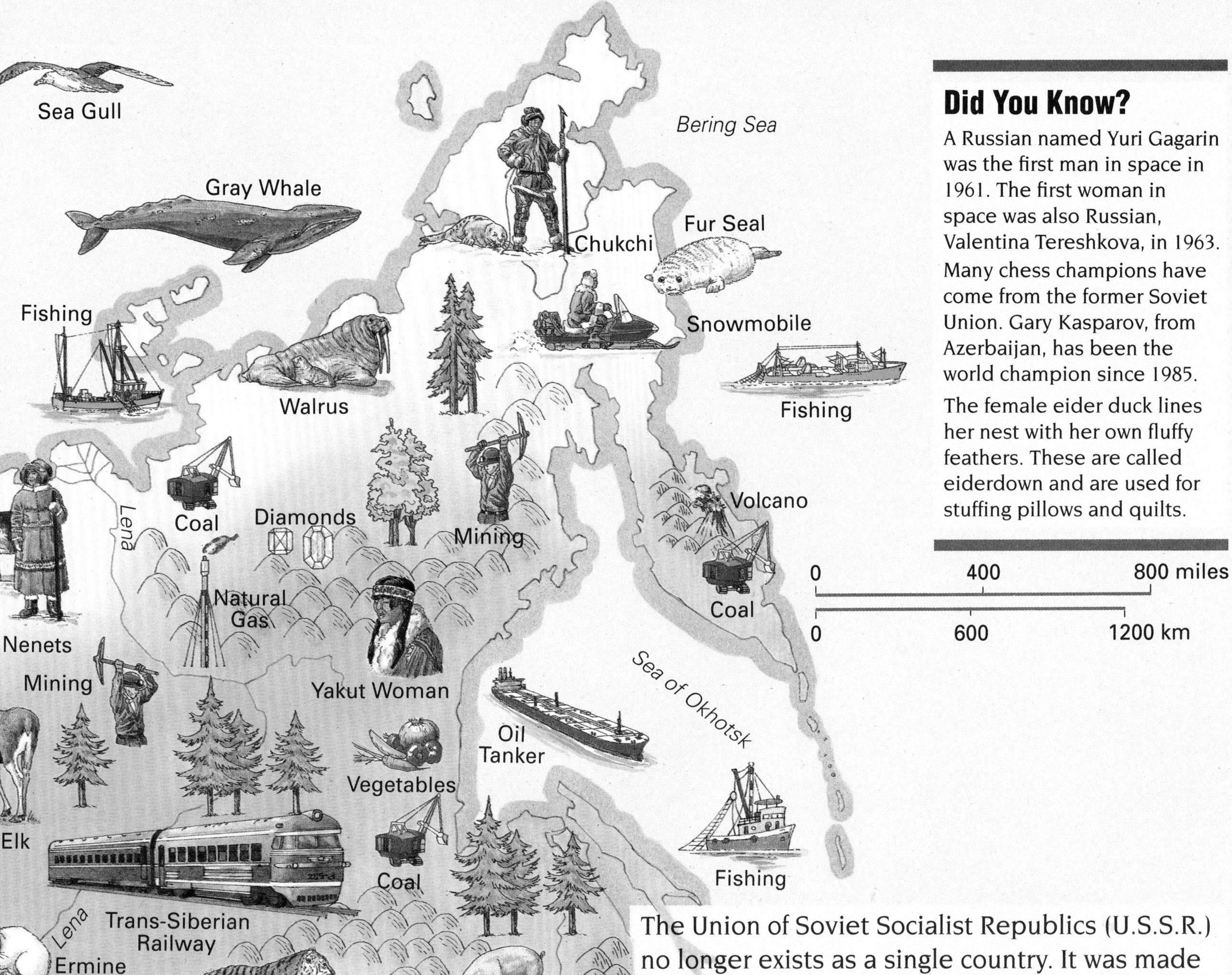

Did You Know?

A Russian named Yuri Gagarin was the first man in space in 1961. The first woman in space was also Russian, Valentina Tereshkova, in 1963.

Many chess champions have come from the former Soviet Union. Gary Kasparov, from Azerbaijan, has been the world champion since 1985.

The female eider duck lines her nest with her own fluffy feathers. These are called eiderdown and are used for stuffing pillows and quilts.

0 400 800 miles

0 600 1200 km

The Union of Soviet Socialist Republics (U.S.S.R.) no longer exists as a single country. It was made up of 15 republics, which are now independent countries. Most of these countries form the new Commonwealth of Independent States (C.I.S.). The largest new country—and the largest country in the world—is Russia. It stretches from Europe, across the Ural Mountains, to northern Asia. In the northeast it is separated from North America by the Bering Strait, a narrow strip of ocean.

The Ural Mountains run from north to south through Russia, separating the continents of Europe and Asia. The European countries have more people and industry than the Asian countries. The richest farmlands are in the southwest. Because of small harvests and poor storage and transport, there have been severe food shortages. The new countries are striving to improve this situation.

More About...

The **Trans-Siberian Railway** runs from Moscow to Vladivostok. It takes 8 days to make the journey.

The **Nenets** are reindeer herders. They live in the north of Russia, near the Arctic. They are an ancient people.

Sturgeon are fish that grow 14 feet long. Their eggs are made into a food called caviar. Caviar is very expensive.

In the Arctic Ocean, huge **ice-breaking ships** plow through the ice. Smaller ships are then able to follow.

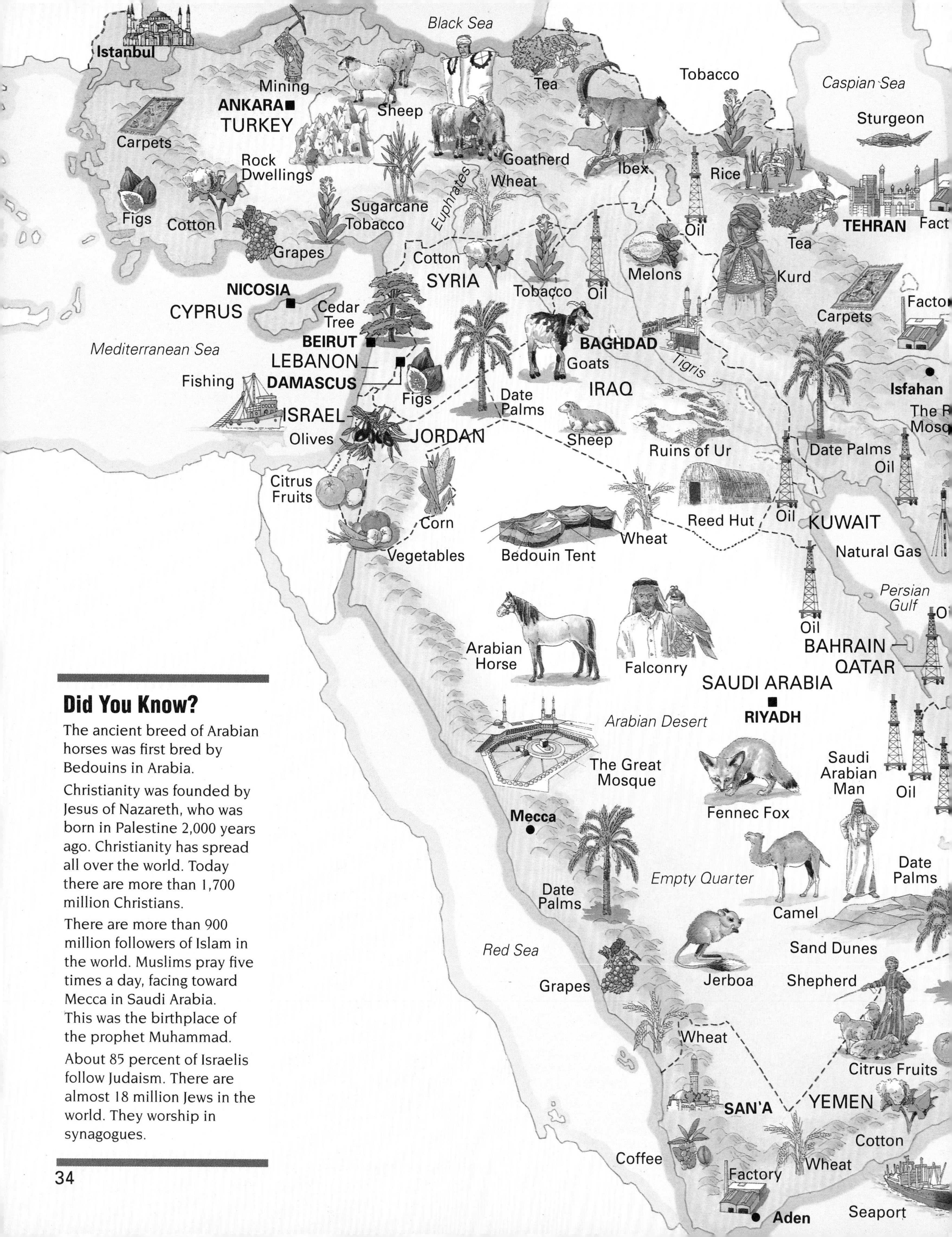

Did You Know?

The ancient breed of Arabian horses was first bred by Bedouins in Arabia.

Christianity was founded by Jesus of Nazareth, who was born in Palestine 2,000 years ago. Christianity has spread all over the world. Today there are more than 1,700 million Christians.

There are more than 900 million followers of Islam in the world. Muslims pray five times a day, facing toward Mecca in Saudi Arabia. This was the birthplace of the prophet Muhammad.

About 85 percent of Israelis follow Judaism. There are almost 18 million Jews in the world. They worship in synagogues.

Middle East

The Middle East covers a large area of southwest Asia and northeast Africa. This region is called the "cradle of civilization" because many ancient civilizations began here. Three world religions also started here—Christianity, Islam, and Judaism. Most people in the Middle East are Muslims, followers of Islam. There are Christians and Jews, too. Most Israelis practice Judaism. The ancient Holy Land of Palestine, which is sacred to people of all three religions, is now occupied by Israel and Jordan.

The vast Arabian Desert covers parts of Saudi Arabia, Jordan, Oman, Yemen, and the United Arab Emirates. The discovery of oil beneath the desert and in the Persian Gulf has made the countries around the gulf rich.

The Middle East has been marked by great unrest in recent years. Religious differences and territorial disputes remain to be solved.

More About . . .

Bedouins are tribes of Arabs who live in the Arabian Desert. Their homes are tents that they move from place to place.

Saudi Arabia has the world's largest reserves of **oil.** The oil is pumped into ships called tankers, which transport it to other countries.

Falconry is a traditional form of hunting in Saudi Arabia. Falcons are birds of prey. They hunt and eat other small animals. In captivity, they are trained to hunt other animals—but only on command.

Kurds live in the mountains where Iran, Iraq, and Turkey meet. They want to form a Kurdish state where they can live by their own rules and customs.

The **ruins of Ur** are in southern Iraq. Ur was one of the most important cities of the ancient Sumerian civilization in Mesopotamia.

A **sand dune** is a ridge of sand formed by the wind. The wind constantly changes the shape of the dune. Part of the Arabian Desert is called the "Empty Quarter." It is the largest stretch of continuous sand in the world.

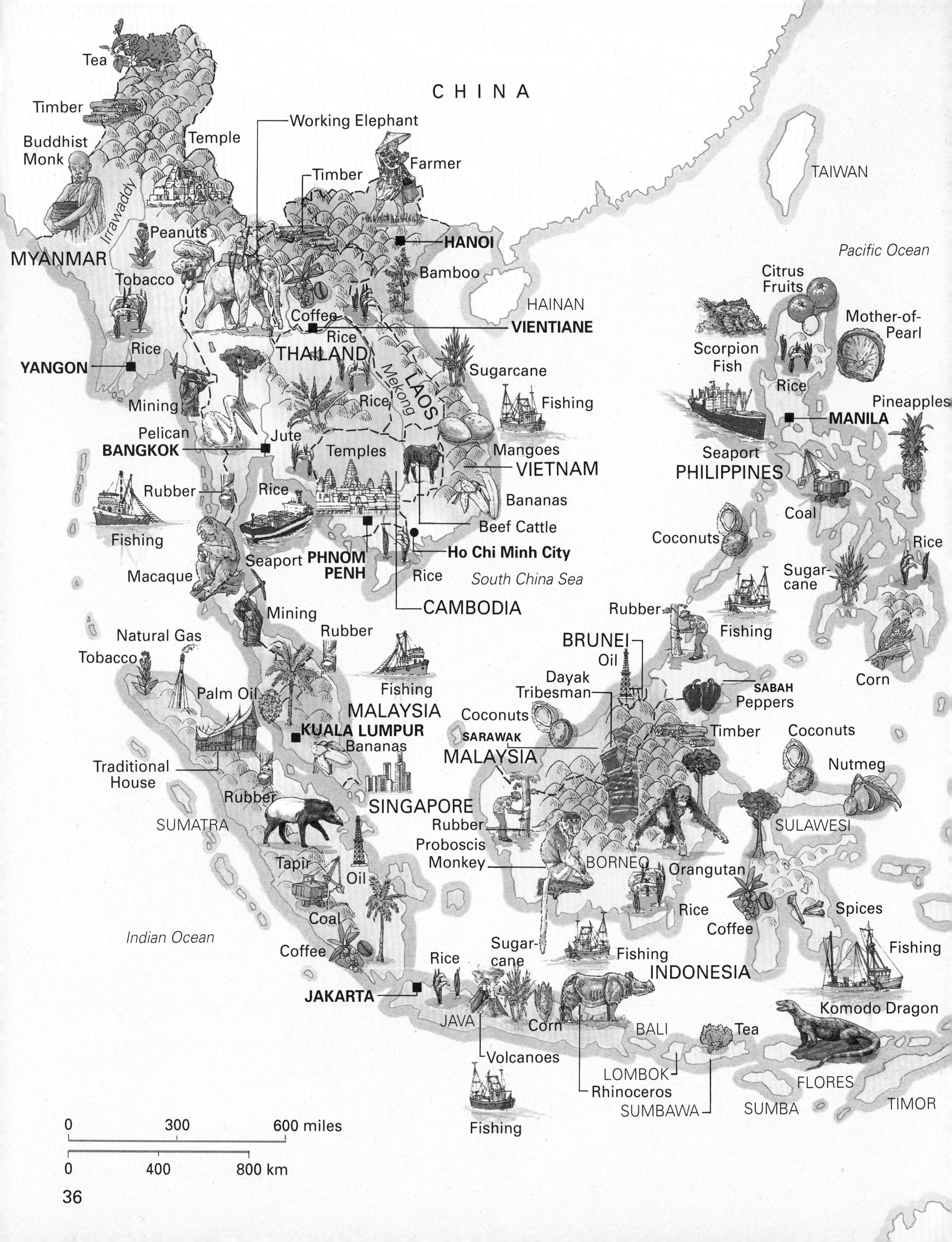
CHINA
Tea
Timber
Buddhist Monk
Temple
Working Elephant
Farmer
Timber
Irrawaddy
Peanuts
MYANMAR
HANOI
Bamboo
Tobacco
TAIWAN
Pacific Ocean
HAINAN
Coffee
VIENTIANE
Rice
Rice
THAILAND
Mekong
LAOS
YANGON
Sugarcane
Mining
Rice
Fishing
Pelican
Jute
BANGKOK
Temples
Mangoes
VIETNAM
Rubber
Rice
Bananas
Fishing
Beef Cattle
Seaport
PHNOM PENH
Ho Chi Minh City
Macaque
Rice
South China Sea
Mining
CAMBODIA
Natural Gas
Rubber
Tobacco
Palm Oil
Fishing
MALAYSIA
KUALA LUMPUR
Bananas
Traditional House
Rubber
SINGAPORE
SUMATRA
Tapir
Oil
Coal
Indian Ocean
Coffee
Rice
JAKARTA
JAVA
Sugar-cane
Corn
Volcanoes
Fishing
Citrus Fruits
Mother-of-Pearl
Scorpion Fish
Rice
Pineapples
MANILA
Seaport
PHILIPPINES
Coal
Coconuts
Rice
Sugar-cane
Rubber
Fishing
BRUNEI
Oil
Corn
Dayak Tribesman
SABAH
Peppers
Coconuts
Timber
Coconuts
SARAWAK
MALAYSIA
Nutmeg
Rubber
Proboscis Monkey
BORNEO
Orangutan
SULAWESI
Rice
Coffee
Spices
Fishing
Fishing
INDONESIA
Komodo Dragon
BALI
Tea
LOMBOK
Rhinoceros
SUMBAWA
FLORES
SUMBA
TIMOR
0
300
600 miles
0
400
800 km

Southeast Asia

Southeast Asia is made up of more than 20,000 islands. Most of these belong to Indonesia and the Philippines. Indonesia's islands are scattered between the Asian mainland and the northern tip of Australia. Much of Southeast Asia is covered by tropical rainforest, and most of the people are farmers who live near the coast and in river valleys. Indonesia, Thailand, Vietnam, and Myanmar (Burma) are among the world's top rice producers. The rainforest provides wood, such as teak and mahogany. Malaysia, Indonesia, and Thailand are the world's leading rubber producers.

Many countries in the region are poor, and most cities are overcrowded. Vietnam, Laos, and Cambodia have all suffered from war. In contrast, the small countries of Brunei and Singapore are both rich.

More About . . .

Most people in Myanmar are Buddhists. Between the ages of 6 and 13, boys in Myanmar spend some time as **monks**. They learn to lead a spiritual life.

The **Komodo dragon** is the largest lizard in the world—it can grow almost 10 feet long. It lives on the Lesser Sunda Islands of Indonesia.

Rice is the region's main crop. In many areas it is grown on terraces, which are broad steps cut into the sides of hills or mountains.

Rubber is made from latex, a milky gum collected from the **rubber tree.** This tree grows in many parts of Southeast Asia.

Timber, especially teak, is an important export in some Southeast Asian countries. It is used abroad for furniture and in shipbuilding.

In Papua New Guinea, people believe in spirits. They build special **spirit houses** to lure any spirits away from their homes.

On Java, material from the eruption of **volcanoes** produces fertile soil for growing crops.

The city of **Singapore** is the capital of the Singapore republic. It is an international port and business center, popular with tourists.

Did You Know?

Malaysia is the world's leading producer of tin. It is also mined in Indonesia and Thailand.

Oil was discovered in Brunei in 1929. The country is ruled by a sultan. He is said to be the world's richest person.

Violent tropical storms called typhoons are common in the Philippines.

In the forests of Thailand, elephants are still used to move felled teak trees.

South Asia

To the north of India rise the snow-covered peaks of the Himalaya Mountains. The kingdoms of Bhutan and Nepal can be found there. While few people live in the mountains, it is very crowded down on the plains of India, Pakistan, and Bangladesh. The Indian cities of Bombay and Calcutta also are home to millions of people. The flat central plains get very dry during the hot season. The rains, when they come, last from June to October.

In Bangladesh, most people are farmers. But the crops are often destroyed by floods. With its rapid population growth and lack of food, Bangladesh is desperately poor and dependent on foreign aid.

The Hindu and Buddhist religions started in south Asia. Today India has large numbers of Hindus, while Pakistan and Bangladesh are mainly Muslim states.

Did You Know?

Tigers once roamed free in India's forests. But these big cats—long hunted for their skin—are now endangered because the forests are being cut down. The tigers that remain are protected by law.

Varanasi is a holy Indian city visited by many pilgrims—Hindus, Buddhists, and others. They come from all over south Asia to bathe in the Ganges River. The Hindus believe the river is sacred and will purify them.

The mongoose is a fierce little animal. It eats frogs, birds, lizards, and their eggs. A mongoose throws the eggs against stones to break their shells. The Indian gray mongoose can kill a cobra.

Although Sherpas are a farming people in Nepal, they often work as guides for climbers in the Himalaya Mountains. One of these guides, Tenzing Norgay, climbed to the top of Mount Everest with the New Zealand explorer Edmund Hillary in 1953. This was the first time anyone had reached the top of the world's highest mountain.

In 1947, India gained freedom from British rule and was divided into 2 independent countries: India and Pakistan.

More About...

Making Afghan **carpets** is a traditional craft. The carpets are made from goat and sheep wool. The wool is dyed and spun. It is then woven on looms.

Mount Everest lies in the Himalaya Mountains. It stands on the border between the countries of Nepal and Tibet. At 29,028 feet, it is the world's highest mountain.

Polo is a sport that has been played in Pakistan for centuries. Two teams of players on horseback try to hit the ball into the goal with their mallets.

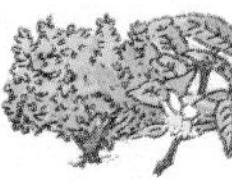

Most **tea** comes from the leaves of a small plant that is widely grown in India and Sri Lanka. The leaves are picked, dried, and then sold, loose or in teabags.

Taj Mahal means "crown of the palace." It was built by Emperor Shah Jahan in memory of his wife.

Hindus believe that **cows** are sacred, so they never kill or eat them. Cows wander freely in city streets.

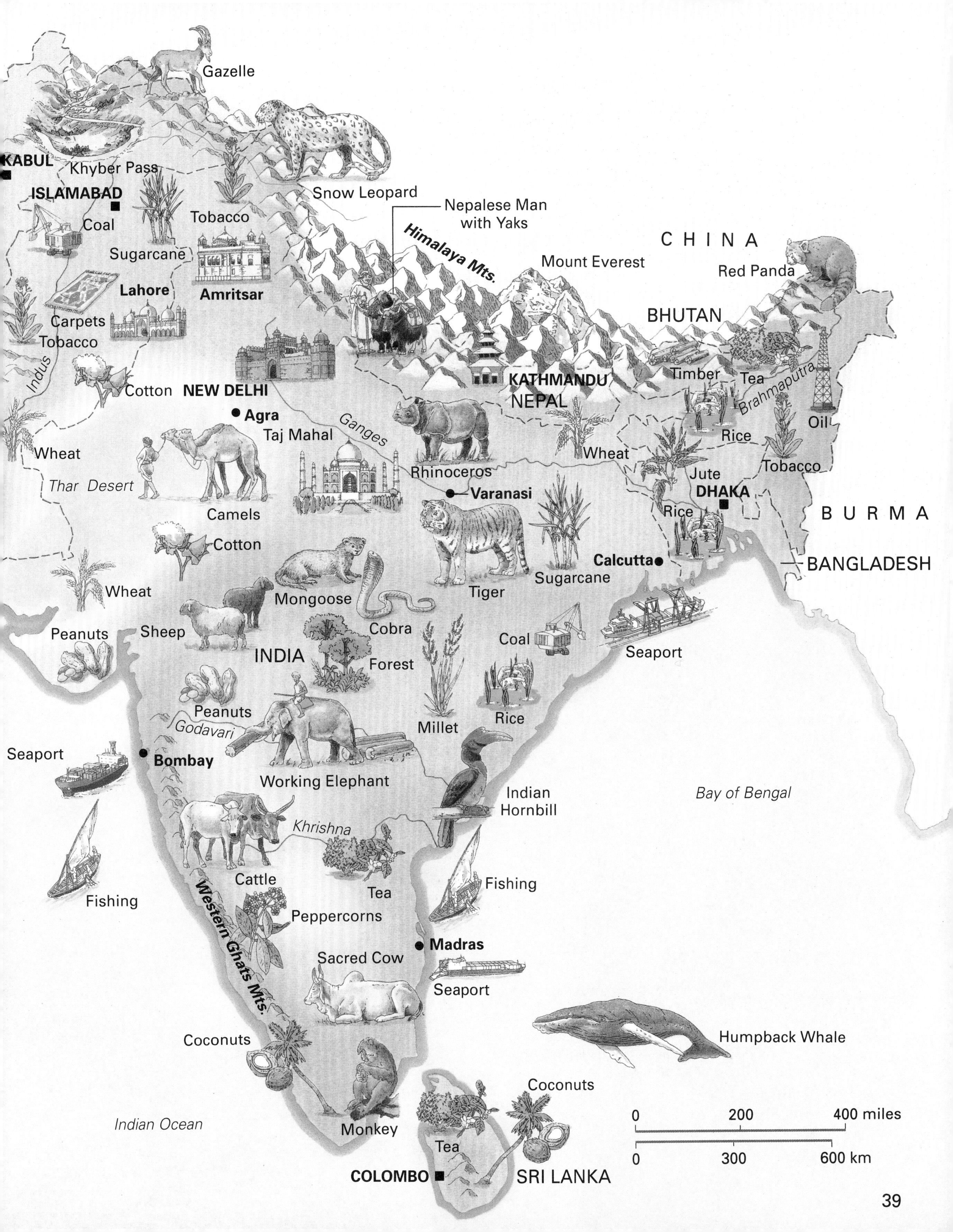

Gazelle
KABUL
Khyber Pass
ISLAMABAD
Snow Leopard
Nepalese Man with Yaks
Coal
Tobacco
Sugarcane
Himalaya Mts.
CHINA
Mount Everest
Red Panda
Lahore
Amritsar
Carpets
Tobacco
BHUTAN
Indus
Cotton
NEW DELHI
KATHMANDU
NEPAL
Timber
Tea
Brahmaputra
Oil
Agra
Taj Mahal
Ganges
Wheat
Rice
Wheat
Rhinoceros
Tobacco
Thar Desert
Jute
Varanasi
DHAKA
Camels
Rice
BURMA
Cotton
Calcutta
BANGLADESH
Sugarcane
Wheat
Mongoose
Tiger
Peanuts
Sheep
Cobra
Coal
Seaport
INDIA
Forest
Peanuts
Godavari
Rice
Millet
Seaport
Bombay
Working Elephant
Indian Hornbill
Bay of Bengal
Khrishna
Cattle
Fishing
Fishing
Tea
Western Ghats Mts.
Peppercorns
Madras
Sacred Cow
Seaport
Humpback Whale
Coconuts
Coconuts
Indian Ocean
Monkey
Tea
COLOMBO
SRI LANKA
0
200
400 miles
0
300
600 km

China and Mongolia

Although China is only a bit larger than the continental U.S., it has more than 4 times as many people. Most of China has so many mountains or is so dry that few people can live in those areas. The others live crowded along the coast, on the plains, and along China's great rivers. The soil around the Huang He—the Yellow River—is ideal for farming.

The capital of China, Beijing, is home to more than 10 million people. Shanghai, the largest city and a center for shipping and industry, has even more people.

Off the southeast coast of mainland China is the island of Taiwan, which is a separate country. North of China is the independent country of Mongolia—land of the Gobi Desert and rolling grasslands. The Mongols are expert horsemen who follow their herds of sheep across the plains.

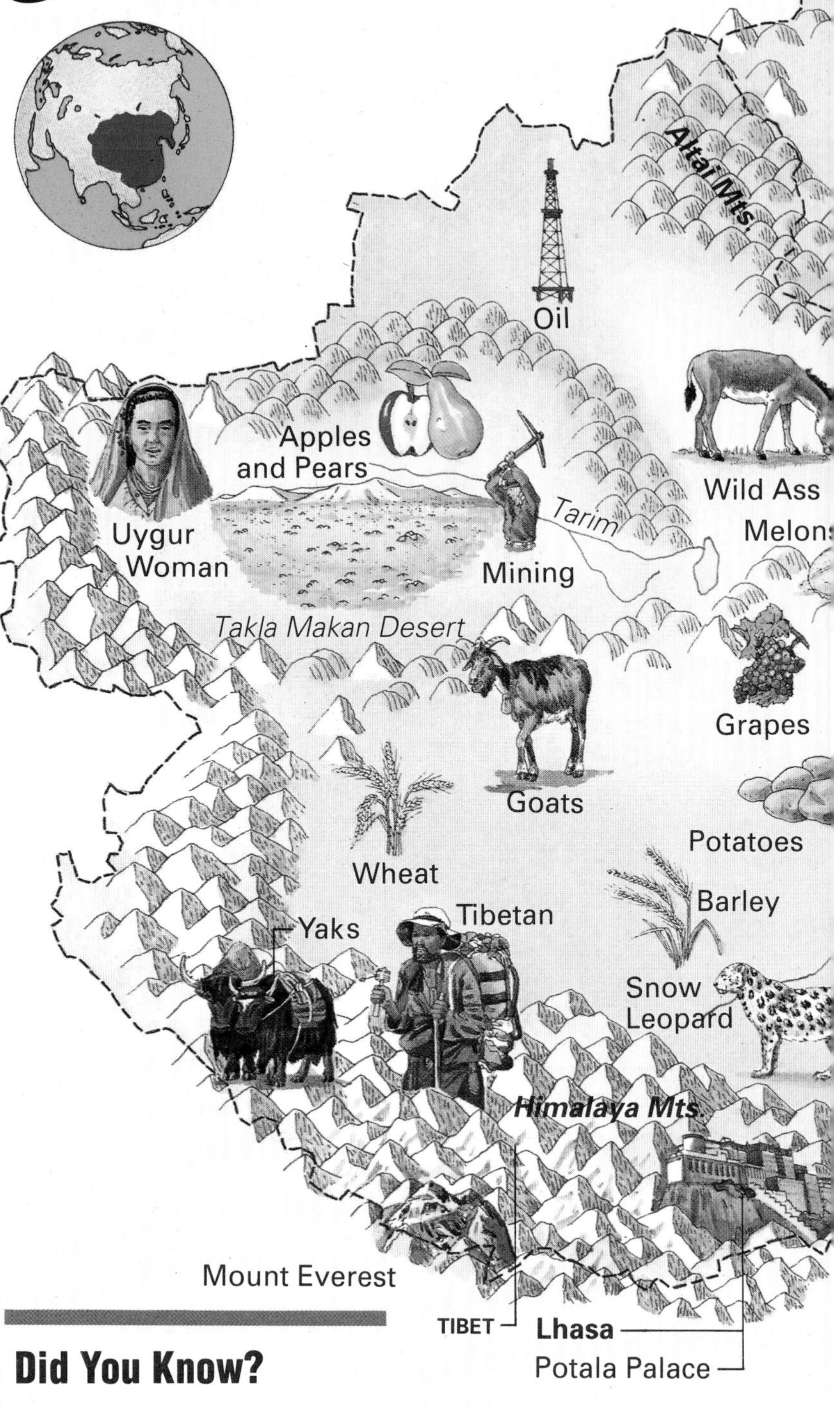

More About . . .

The **yak** is a mountain ox that lives in the Himalayas. Yaks have long horns and shaggy hair. Tibetans use yak milk to make sour butter, which is traditionally served in tea.

The **Great Wall** of China was first built in about 214 B.C. to defend the ancient Chinese empire from its enemies in the north. It is 1,400 miles long and can be seen from the moon!

Bamboo is the giant of all grasses, growing as tall as some trees. Bamboo supplies food for giant pandas that live in China's bamboo forests.

Set high on a hill, the **Potala Palace** towers above the city of Lhasa in Tibet. It has 1,000 rooms. It was once the home of the Dalai Lama, Tibet's leader. Lhasa is holy to Tibetan Buddhists.

The two-humped **Bactrian camels** are found in the deserts of China and Mongolia. Their thick fur and stocky bodies help them survive the cold winters. Unfortunately, they are almost extinct in the wild.

Mongols live in round tents of felt, which they call ***gers***. They tie their gers on the backs of camels when they travel.

Did You Know?

In China, each year is named after an animal. 1993 is the year of the cockerel. 1994 is the year of the dog. 2000 is the year of the dragon.

There are over 130 million bicycles in China. About 30 million new bikes are made each year.

Hong Kong, with its magnificent harbor, is a leading commercial center.

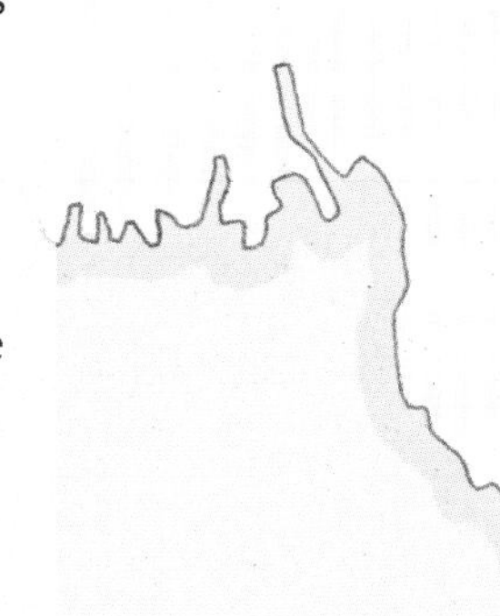

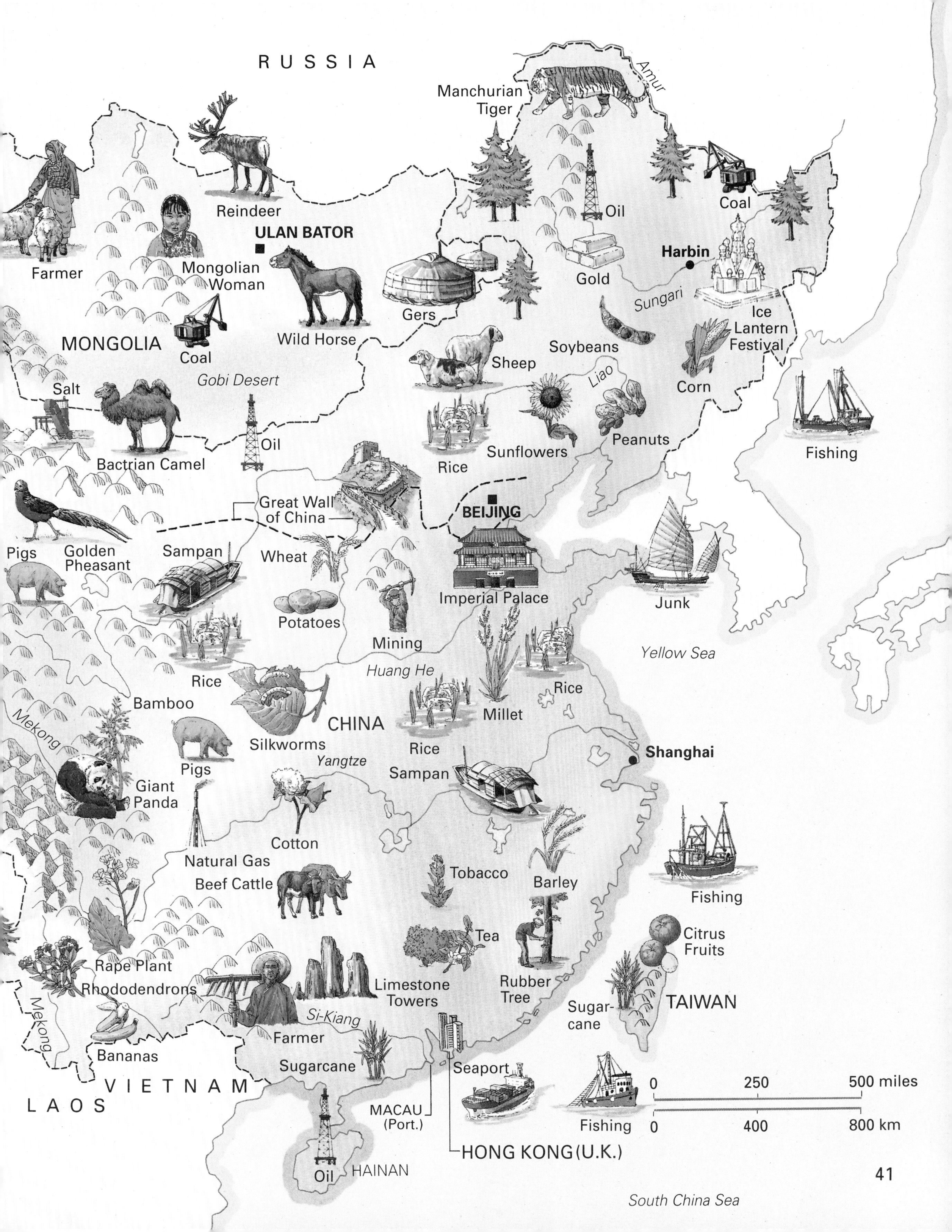
RUSSIA
Amur
Manchurian Tiger
Reindeer
Farmer
Mongolian Woman
ULAN BATOR
Wild Horse
Gers
Oil
Gold
Coal
Harbin
Sungari
Ice Lantern Festival
MONGOLIA
Coal
Gobi Desert
Soybeans
Sheep
Corn
Liao
Salt
Bactrian Camel
Oil
Rice
Sunflowers
Peanuts
Fishing
Great Wall of China
BEIJING
Imperial Palace
Junk
Pigs
Golden Pheasant
Sampan
Wheat
Potatoes
Mining
Yellow Sea
Rice
Huang He
Millet
Rice
Bamboo
Mekong
Silkworms
CHINA
Rice
Shanghai
Pigs
Giant Panda
Yangtze
Sampan
Cotton
Natural Gas
Beef Cattle
Tobacco
Barley
Fishing
Tea
Citrus Fruits
Rape Plant
Rhododendrons
Limestone Towers
Rubber Tree
Sugar-cane
TAIWAN
Mekong
Si-Kiang
Farmer
Bananas
Sugarcane
Seaport
VIETNAM
LAOS
MACAU (Port.)
HONG KONG (U.K.)
Fishing
0
250
500 miles
0
400
800 km
Oil
HAINAN
South China Sea

Japan and Korea

Japan consists of 4 main islands: Hokkaidō, Honshū, Shikoku, and Kyūshū. There are more than 3,000 smaller islands, but most of these are uninhabited. A chain of volcanic mountains runs across Japan, and there are often earthquakes. The southern islands are hot and damp, while the northern islands are colder. Much of the land is covered with mountains and forests. Rice is the main crop. Fishing is also important. Japan is the world's leading maker of ships, cars, and electronic equipment. Most Japanese enjoy a high standard of living.

Korea lies to the west of Japan. In North Korea the winters are very cold, and the climate is suitable for growing potatoes and corn. Mining and industry are important there. South Korea has a warmer climate. Most South Koreans are farmers, but the country has many factories and its products are exported all over the world.

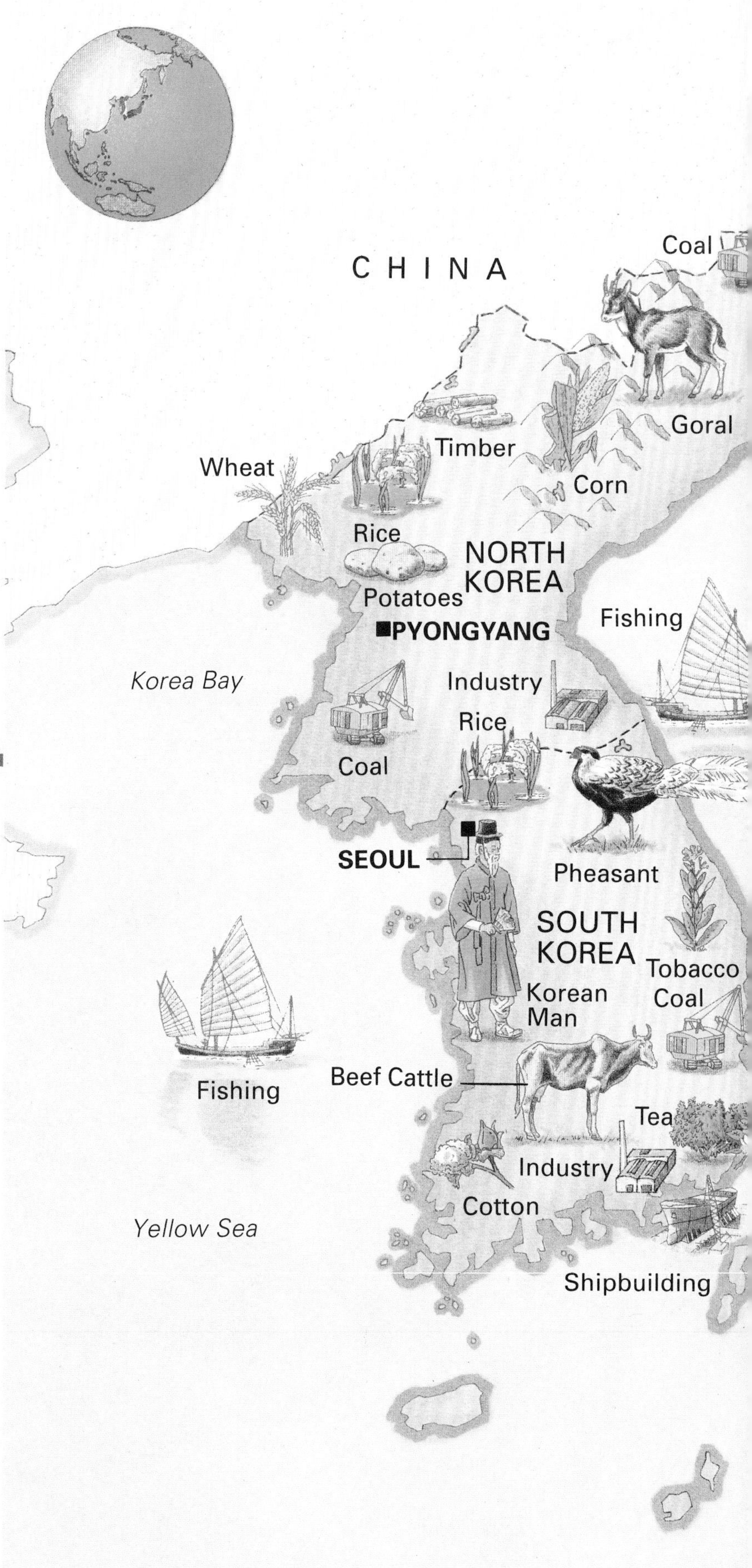

Did You Know?

The Japanese pay special attention to nature. In Japanese gardens, rocks, pools, and waterfalls are used to create landscapes.

The cherry blossom is the national flower of Japan. Every spring people come to Ōsaka to see the cherry trees in bloom. People sit in special pavilions to enjoy the beauty of the scenery.

There are more than 100 daily newspapers in Japan, and nearly 40 million copies are sold each day. There are also 2,700 magazines.

Most of Japan's population live in towns and cities. Eleven Japanese cities have more than a million people.

In the Kinki area of Japan, fishermen use cormorants as helpers. The birds are attached to the boats by long ropes. They dive into the water after fish, but rings placed around their necks prevent them from swallowing their catch.

Mount Fuji is a volcano that towers above five beautiful lakes. It last erupted in 1707. Many Japanese believe Mount Fuji is sacred.

Visitors to a Japanese home are expected to take off their shoes and leave them at the door. Guest slippers are provided for walking in hallways, but must be removed in rooms with straw mats on the floor.

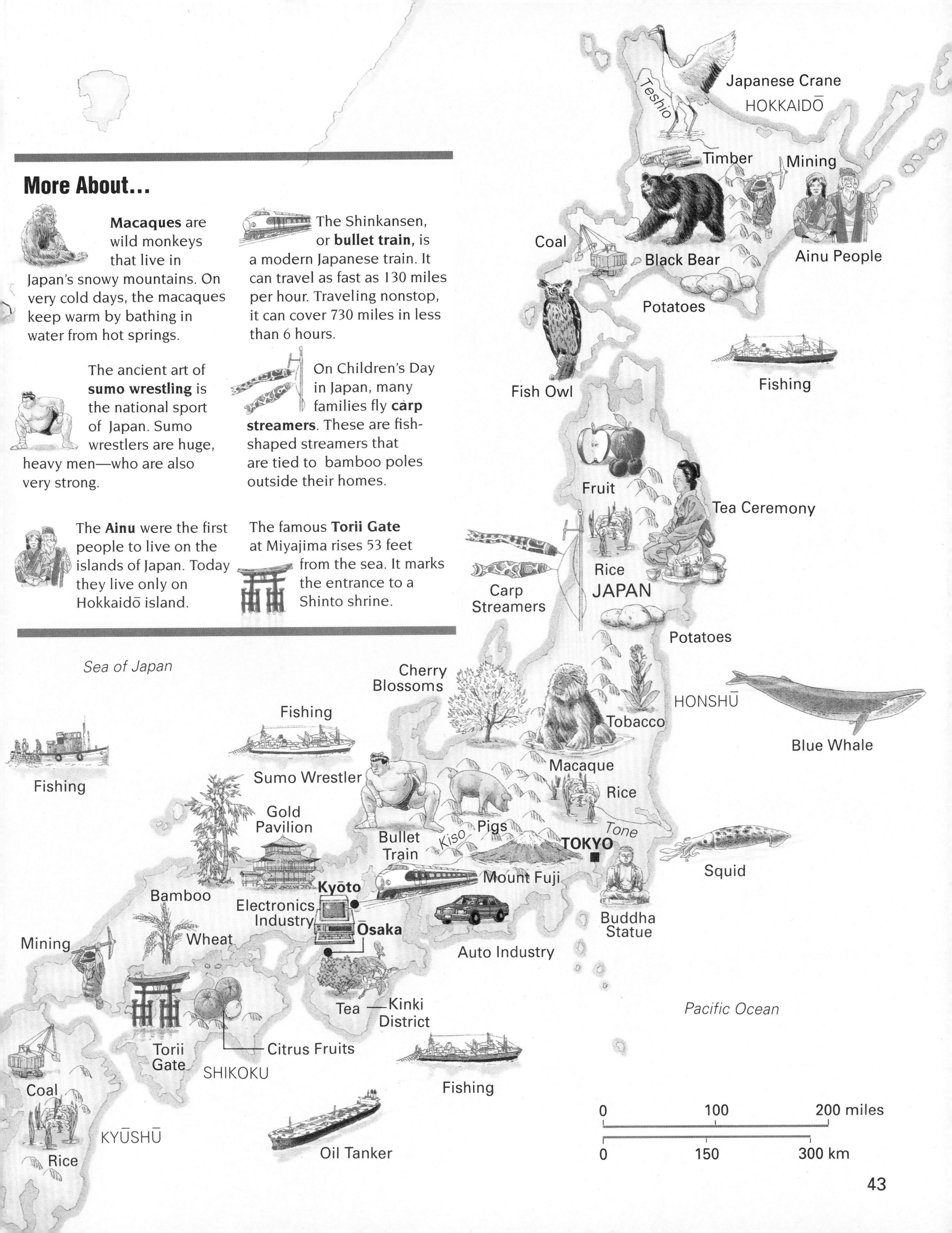

More About...

Macaques are wild monkeys that live in Japan's snowy mountains. On very cold days, the macaques keep warm by bathing in water from hot springs.

The Shinkansen, or **bullet train,** is a modern Japanese train. It can travel as fast as 130 miles per hour. Traveling nonstop, it can cover 730 miles in less than 6 hours.

The ancient art of **sumo wrestling** is the national sport of Japan. Sumo wrestlers are huge, heavy men—who are also very strong.

On Children's Day in Japan, many families fly **carp streamers**. These are fish-shaped streamers that are tied to bamboo poles outside their homes.

The **Ainu** were the first people to live on the islands of Japan. Today they live only on Hokkaidō island.

The famous **Torii Gate** at Miyajima rises 53 feet from the sea. It marks the entrance to a Shinto shrine.

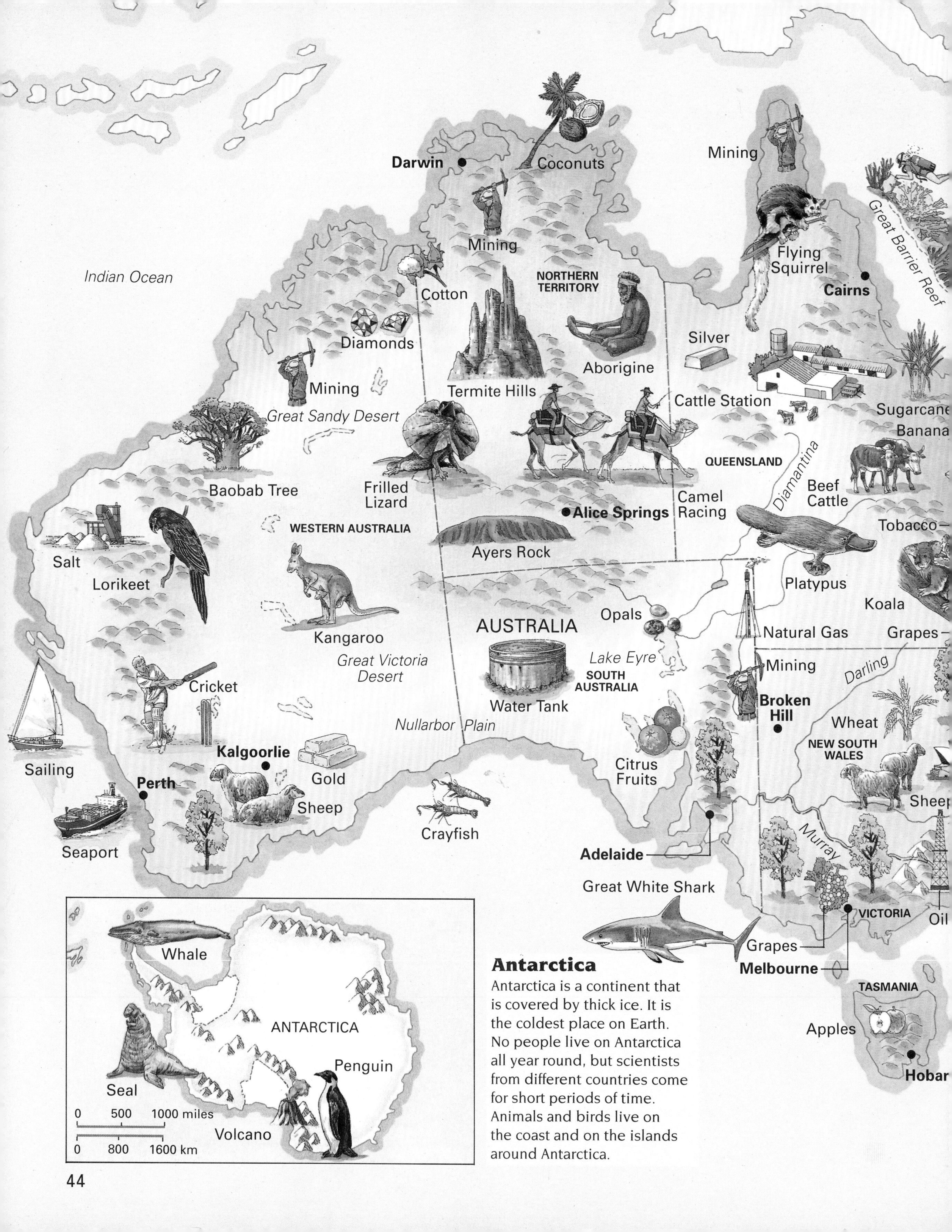

Antarctica

Antarctica is a continent that is covered by thick ice. It is the coldest place on Earth. No people live on Antarctica all year round, but scientists from different countries come for short periods of time. Animals and birds live on the coast and on the islands around Antarctica.

Australasia and **Antarctica**

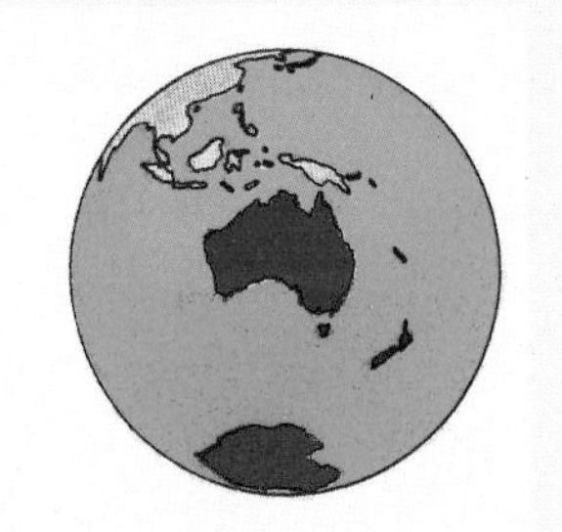

Australia and New Zealand are part of the region of Australasia. Much of western Australia is hot desert and few people live there. Many people live along the eastern coast, where the climate is cooler. Sydney, Australia's largest city, is on the coast. In the center of Australia is the outback, a dry, hot grassland where sheep are raised. Australia is the world's principal wool producer. Mining is important, too. Rich deposits of minerals, such as gold, silver, gemstones, and iron ore, are found here.

New Zealand is southeast of Australia and has a milder climate. It is divided into two main islands—North Island and South Island. Most New Zealanders live on North Island, where there are more large cities. South Island has good grazing land and dairy farming is important.

More About . . .

Kangaroos belong to a group of animals called marsupials. Marsupials have pouches of skin where their babies are carried after they are born.

Cricket is a sport that is as popular with Australians as baseball is with Americans. Australian and British teams often compete.

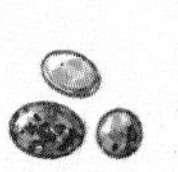

Almost all the world's **opals** come from Australia. Opals are valued as gemstones, and they are also used in industry.

The **Great Barrier Reef** is the biggest coral reef in the world. It runs along the Queensland coast for 1,250 miles. The reef is very popular with divers.

The Maoris, descended from the first settlers in New Zealand, are known for their **wood carvings**—one of the traditions the Maoris are trying hard to keep alive.

The **kiwi** lives in the forests of New Zealand. This odd-looking, flightless bird uses its long bill to dig for earthworms.

Did You Know?

Before Europeans arrived in 1770, the aborigines were the only people in Australia. Aborigines roamed the continent, hunting and gathering food, for at least 30,000 years. The land is still sacred to them, and their legend about its creation is called Dreamtime.

The baobab is a type of bottle tree. Its swollen trunk stores water to help it live through the dry season.

Ayers Rock rises 1,143 feet above the central Australian desert. To the aborigines, this vast red rock is a sacred place called Uluru. At the rock's base are caves, which have paintings on the walls.

Map Index

Illustrations by Illustratori Associati Boni-Galante (Simone Boni, L. R. Galante, Lorenzo Cecchi, Lorenzo Pieri, Paola Ravaglia)